MAN'S EMERGING MIND

N. J. BERRILL

MAN'S EMERGING MIND

MAN'S PROGRESS THROUGH TIME—
TREES, ICE, FLOOD, ATOMS AND THE UNIVERSE

DODD, MEAD & COMPANY · New York

Printed in the United States of America
Apollo Edition

To my children

and to Jacquelyn

PREFACE

IN this book I have drawn upon such resources in writing and from my own experience that I can muster, but my indebtedness is primarily to humanity itself, both present and past. At the same time I would like to offer a statement which was written by Ana María O'Neill soon after the explosion of the first atomic bomb 'in this hour of crisis, in which science is about to lose its freedom,' to use her own words. It gives point to what I have attempted in sketching the outline of the man-nature event and is in part as follows:

"In order that man may be persuaded to put forth the intense effort required to change chaos into order, he *must* feel that he has the necessary stature for the assignment, at least the potentialities . . . It may appear absurd to philosophers, but in our age of specialization it is not only man's concept of matter which must come from science, but also man's concept of himself . . . At the stage of specialization of our knowledge, to determine what is specifically human in man requires a veritable cracking of the concept of man. This cracking, in its turn, requires a concentrated effort of specialists; as much as was required for the atomic bomb . . . If the concept is cracked, the release of spiritual energy will be voluminous enough to make physical nuclear energy behave. It might be powerful enough to light the lamps of peace and keep them burning." Accordingly what I have written in the following pages is the point of view of a biologist who has specialized in the study of living organisms with particular interest in their development. As a concept of man it is incomplete, but it is one man's contribution.

PRELUDE

'I am that living and fiery essence of the divine substance that
glows in the beauty of the fields. I shine in the water, I burn in
the sun and the moon and the stars . . . I breathe in the verdure
and in the flowers, and when the waters flow like living things, it
is I . . . I am Wisdom. Mine is the blast of the thundered Word
by which all things were made . . . I am Life.'

> *Hildegarde of Bingen* (1098–1180)
> *in "The Mind and the Eye" by Agnes Arbor*

'the universe itself does not hold life cheaply. Life is a rare
occurrence among the billions of galaxies and solar systems that
occupy space. And in this particular solar system life occurs on
only one planet. And on that planet life takes millions of forms.
Of all those countless forms of life, only one, the human species,
possesses certain faculties in combination that give it supreme
advantages over all the others. Among those faculties or gifts is
a creative intelligence that enables man to reflect, anticipate, and
speculate, to encompass past experience and also to visualize
future needs. There are endless other wondrous faculties the
mechanisms of which are not yet within the understanding of

their beneficiaries—the faculties of hope, conscience, appreciation of beauty, kinship, love, faith.'

Norman Cousins
in "Who Speaks for Man?"

'Human life is driven forward by its dim apprehension of notions too general for its existing language.'

Alfred North Whitehead

'Never before today has the integrity of the intimate, the detailed, the true art, the integrity of craftmanship and the preservation of the familiar, of the humorous and the beautiful stood in more massive contrast to the vastness of life, the greatness of the globe, the otherness of people, the otherness of ways and the all-encompassing dark . . . this balance, this perpetual, precarious, impossible balance between the infinitely open and the intimate, this time—our twentieth century—has been long in coming; but it has come. It is, I think, for us and our children, the only way.'

J. Robert Oppenheimer

'He who kisses the joy as it flies
Lives in Eternity's sunrise.'

William Blake

CONTENTS

1

I WHO SPEAK

I AM a human being, whatever that may be. I speak for all of us who move and think and feel and whom time consumes. I speak as an individual unique in a universe beyond my understanding, and I speak for man. I am hemmed in by limitations of sense and mind and body, of place and time and circumstance, some of which I know but most of which I do not. I am like a man journeying through a forest, aware of occasional glints of light overhead, with recollections of the long trail I have already traveled, and conscious of wider spaces ahead. I want to see more clearly where I have been and where I am going, and above all I want to know why I am where I am and why I am traveling at all. I, John Berrill, a selfconscious fragment of life, want to know; and this book is an exploration and an inquiry for my own satisfaction and for any who wish to come with me.

Our scientific age is an age of extension of the senses by means of instruments, and because of this torrents of new and novel information pour in—and we are trying to put it together and to turn the new searchlights towards our own status, past, present and future. This need to understand the nature of things has found expression in the cosmogonies of the religious creeds of all mankind and in some form perhaps ever since we first learned to communicate thought by means of speech. It is the great conversation, one that started long before the dawn of recorded history and that becomes more animated all the time/ For too many the discussion is already closed, with full acceptance of the dogma of particular religions. For the rest it is wide open, for the origin, nature and destiny of man are problems inadequately solved by the philosophers, religious or otherwise, of the ancient world, whether or not their answers survive in contemporary form.

I suppose a newborn babe has always seemed to be more or less a miracle to those who first gazed upon it, and not only to its parents. There it is in all its squawling presence and awesome potentiality. Birth is a dramatic arrival, not unlike the rabbit that pops out of the magician's hat when he whips his kerchief away. Yet I believe the masking of the earlier events prevents us from appreciating the true wonder of creation. My particular concern as a biologist has been the study of the development of organisms generally, and perhaps because of this preoccupation I have become acutely conscious of myself in the same manner as I have looked upon other kinds of life.

Birth itself is a somewhat arbitrary shift from the womb to a more exposed existence in the world at large. It does not represent any special climax in the process of growth as a whole and under somewhat different circumstances might occur considerably sooner or later. We usually fail however to sense the almost unbelievable event of our becoming. I find it difficult to put together the sequence of images of what I know myself to have been at various times following my conception. It is like an attempt to make a movie out of a score of separate frames and only when you flip them fast enough do you get the sense of motion and continuous change. My own capacity for visual imagery and projection has its limits, but it is im-

portant I think to try to get the whole picture of a man and
not to commence looking when eight or nine pounds of human infant is already in view. The greater fantasy takes place
much earlier.

I wish I could bring sharply before your eyes the whole
course of development of a human being from the first splitting of the egg to the full bloom of maturity. We need not
only to see what goes on during development in this darkness
of the womb but to speed up the process as in the movies now
made of the growth and unfolding of flowers. For to my mind
the steady expansion of the human organism from a barely
visible speck of protoplasm to the one hundred and fifty
pounds of brawn and brain of the grown adult is startling and
magnificent. On another time-scale it would seem like an explosion, so great is the increase in matter and complexity. We
should keep it in mind when we attempt to define what it
means to be a human. More than this, the most profound
changes of all occur during the period it takes the egg of less
than one hundredth of an inch across to grow to an embryo
about one quarter of an inch long. We do more climbing up
the so-called family tree during this episode than during all the
rest of our enormous growth and long life time put together.

When we speak of the individual human being, if it is to
have full meaning, I am sure we must include the whole and
not any particular stage such as the mature adult. You and I
are organisms that endure with a persisting individuality, yet
withal continually transforming from the microscopic egg to
the final disintegration some seventy to eighty years later. And
organisms I feel certain are as characteristic a product of this
universe as the planets that bear them. We can in fact look
upon man as an organism pure and simple, or we can regard
him as a certain kind of animal, as a warm-blooded mammal,
or we can look for more than this and concentrate upon the
spirit. All of these points of view are valid, but none to the

exclusion of the rest.

A poet wrote that man is a spirit and symbols are his meat. A zoologist states that man is a large, naked, erect biped with a big brain. Neither is wrong for in a sense they are the two sides of the same penny. The trouble here is the common one of the 'nothing but' attitudes. Man is a spirit and man is an animal, the one is as certain as the other and we have little to gain and much to lose by forgetting either of them. We cannot even safely say that the duality of spirit and animal covers the whole reality—words are themselves treacherous and moreover our brains are the product of a peculiar set of circumstances and may all too likely contain built-in blinkers, as if we carry a torch in the darkness and cannot see beyond the margin of the light. Our humanness itself is hard to define, simply in terms of what distinguishes us from all other animals. To say that we have a soul and the rest do not begs the question and is at least debatable. Perhaps we should ask instead how much of a soul and start admitting dogs and chipmunks into the kingdom of heaven. It would better befit our station.

It is simple enough to describe a man in certain ways, to say that he is so big, that he walks on two legs in place of four, has a pair of eyes and so many toes and so on. It amounts to a visual sketch and supplies a recognisable portrait of a kind which would distinguish him from an elephant or a shark. But it would leave out what all we who live have in common, which is the sheer quality of a flame. From the moment of conception until we die, we burn as literally as a candle. This is no casual simile for we both consume and are consumed, and death comes when the process stops. As long as we live, as in the case of the candle, oxygen and other substances are drawn in, take their place and burn with the release of energy and other end products, until at last the process of replacement drops below consumption and the flame of life and candle flicker out. The shape, color and heat of the candle flame is simply the pattern of the continuing action, like the shape of a whirlpool, and it is this quality that makes life so elusive when you try to pin it down. Yet we need to comprehend it. For virtually every atom and molecule in the body is periodically replaced. Those one to two hundred pounds of matter that show up on your bathroom scales are for the most part not the same pounds that weighed them down a few years ago. Every tissue and cell is continually being either rebuilt or replaced, whether skin, blood, hair or bone, and those bald spots and retreating hairlines are less a case of hair falling out than of new hair failing to grow in place of old.

The most remarkable part of it all is that in spite of this continual flux of matter that constitutes my physical being, I am aware of personal continuity, while friends whom I meet again after a ten year absence still recognise me. And yet they do notice a difference. I am familiar, recognisable, it is true, but I am not what I used to be—only approximately so. Chief Justice Holmes wrote that "we must all be born again atom by atom from hour to hour, or perish all at once beyond repair." The truth of this is shown clearly by many recent experiments on the human body in which radio-active tracer substances obtained from the atomic energy laboratories have been used to determine the rate of turn over. The atoms of iron in the blood, of phosphorus in the bone and teeth, iodine in the thyroid gland, all obey the rule—here today, gone tomorrow! Together they all tick away like a biological clock, which in fact is exactly what they amount to. And as the clock ticks, its face changes. I doubt if anyone who knew me only when I was two or three years old could recognise me now. We do change and altogether in a remarkable manner. So who are you and who am I? I know that I am all of me, all that has gone on from the first moment in the womb until the present and is as yet unfinished, for you cannot define what an organism is, any organism, whether it be man, mouse or ameba, unless both time and change are included as well as space and substance. And unless we hold on to this idea we will not be able to describe what it means to be a human being, at least not with any biological meaning. We are creatures of time in more ways than one, and time is of the essence. It is also tiresome, for I cannot talk of more than one thing at a time, with words threaded like beads on a string, which makes any portrayal of the human organism in its multi-dimensional complexity about as satisfactory as a talking record of a sunset. This is one of those limitations I had in mind.

It is not easy to see the whole man or the whole woman with any sense of completeness even or perhaps particularly when it is oneself. I have tried to do so in recent months, putting together what I know of myself, the feeling of change, the memory that takes one back far into pre-school days, and the acquaintance I have with the nature and appearance of embryos of all sizes, whether of humans or of other mammals that resemble them so closely in their earliest stages. It leaves me profoundly impressed by the magnitude of the changes in structure and function and, more than that, by the changing nature of time itself.

What about time? Diogenes said it is the image of eternity, yet that small part of eternal time you and I are individually conscious of is piteously short. Three score years and ten has long been recognized as the span of a man's life, and those lucky or unlucky few that manage to reach a century merely emphasize the usual limit. And still we are blessed with more real time than any other living creature and cursed with enough awareness and intelligence to measure it.

If we merely count our years we find ourselves outdistanced, for a tortoise may live two centuries, while the redwoods of the High Sierras have lived as individual trees for three to four thousand years—and God and posterity forgive us if we cut them all down. Yet the time for living is more than the number of trips around the sun, although this will serve when all other things are equal. If we compare ourselves with other warmblooded mammals of comparable size, such as baboons or goats, we come out very favorably, for thirty years is a pretty ripe age for the great host of hairy folk. Even those disturbing caricatures the chimpanzees, gorillas and orang-utans die off in their fourth decade, while mice and shrews are senile after a year or so. On any reckoning in fact save that of the largest trees or of an overly sluggish reptile we have an unusual amount of time to spend, even more than the elephant and far more than any whale. In many ways it is the essence of our humanity.

Yet this is only a rough and ready appraisal, for a day, a month or a year have no constant meaning. They merely mark off time by the turning of the earth about its axis, the moon about the earth, or the spin of the earth around the sun. If we lived on Venus we would make a faster circuit, reckon with a shorter year and count many more of them before we die. Spinning planets tick off one kind of time, useful for regulating our daily lives, but it is not living time. Real time for us is measured by the beating of a heart, not by the ticking of a clock or the rising and setting of the sun. Yet living time plays tricks on us and starts doing so even before we are born, for a heart beats according to its own measure, with a rest after every beat. With each beat we are just a little bit older, and what may seem paradoxical is true: the younger we are the faster we grow old. At birth the heart beats around 140 times a minute. Even at that it is already slowing down and it continues to do so until the age of 25 when it levels off at about 70 per minute with the body at rest. Does the heart beat a certain number of times and then stop from sheer exhaustion? If so, we would have a fair index of age and you and I would be middle-aged in the true biological sense of time when the heart half the number of times it is capable of. For certain lower forms of life this principle undoubtedly holds, but if we apply it to ourselves it places middle age closer to thirty than forty, which puts my physiological age higher than I am willing to admit. Actually the peak of performance of the heart and circulatory system from the point of view of adaptation and capacity for effort comes at the age of fourteen or fifteen. Thereafter we pay more heavily for accomplishment.

The great days of childhood belong to the past and even my skin is aware of the change, for time itself changes with the time of life and counts for less as time goes on. When I was ten a skin wound of a certain area would have healed in twenty days; at twenty it would have taken thirty one days; now at fifty it should take seventy eight days, supposing I cared sufficiently to make the painful experiment; and in another ten years it should take one hundred days. Living time is a flowing stream and not only skin but the flow of blood confirms it. For while the rate of heart beat is some index of age and a measure of time, it does not indicate the level of actual work.

From the point of view of the body itself the rate of blood flow is more significant than how fast the pump is working, and one of the small assets of the atomic age is that we can introduce the harmless radioactive tracer salts into the circulation and keep track of the flow by means of a Geiger counter. And it is the story of the skin all over again. While at twenty the flow requires twenty seconds to travel from arm vein to the chest region, it takes twice as long at forty and three times as long at sixty. Skin healing and blood flow slow down steadily throughout life and express the slow waning of the vital flame.

There are other changes of course. As the teenage comes to an end the round youthfulness of the face disappears and the fat starts to descend slowly, like a glacier, until somewhere in the middle ages it reaches bottom. And not only hens get tough. Year by year the tissues in general retain less and less water and elasticity disappears. It starts sooner than you think and the fact that I have had to use glasses for reading during the last few years indicates merely a stage in the hardening of the lens that began long ago. It is all part of a progressive process of dehydration that affects every part of us; and as the lens slowly loses water it hardens. A child can see clearly at any distance and usually holds print so close to its nose that it almost squints. But by the time a boy or girl is nine or ten the distance for comfortable reading has already increased and from then on becomes greater with increasing age. Between the ages of forty and fifty the shift becomes more striking and most of us are better off with reading glasses. And the age at which this discomfort first begins to bother you has been used as a basis for predicting how long an individual may expect to live, unless some sudden conflicts with germs or the force of gravity intervenes.

When you and I were seventeen may have been a crisis in our adolescent life, but when we were three or four weeks old, reckoning from conception, was a much more crucial stage. I find it the most fascinating stage of all, for not only are we all there in every important way, in spite of the miniature scale, but it is almost impossible at this stage to distinguish the human embryo from that of any other mammal, whether it be an elephant or a mouse, a rabbit or a chimpanzee. They all look alike, and only slowly and gradually do the essential differences become apparent.

I have often heard the statement that during its life history an animal "climbs up its family tree." It has much in common with the one that says a man passes through a fish stage during his early development within the womb. To ask whether such statements are true is like asking if it is true that you are sober today. A simple affirmative answer is inadequate and a negative one is even worse.

We begin our individual lives in the old-fashioned way as a

solitary cell living and growing in a briny fluid. And from then on, until we are born and start to walk around, we develop in a fashion which echoes the evolutionary journey that took our ancestors a thousand million years to accomplish. Yet our own development is far from being a straightforward condensation of the old interminable story. In the first place there is no time for it in the course of the nine months of prenatal life, and in the second the main business of the human egg is to develop into a human being able to walk around and raise his voice. Every conceivable short cut appears to be taken and departures and innovations occur at every turn. Time itself gets out of joint and certain things that must have come fairly late in the course of evolution show up very early in development. After all, when you build a modern house out of old materials you use them as they are needed, although the old beams and stones carry along their story. In constructing the human being, as in building the house, the old materials have become disarranged and we do not find a fish stage or reptile stage in the literal sense of finding fish or reptile shapes, but we do find structures that mean fish and reptile. The developing skeleton shows this as clearly as any.

The first sign of it in the human embryo is a rod of cells lying in the position of the backbone-to-be and called the notochord. It is a famous rod of tissue and once was the subject of a sermon preached in Westminster Abbey by a scientifically-minded dean. It was the original and all-sufficient skeleton of our earliest forbears, and in all backboned animals, including ourselves, it is the first trace of one to appear in the embryo. In human embryos however we have to look at the very earliest stages to find it, for it is recognisable only in embryos a fraction of an inch long. It still amazes me to realise that I was ever so minute but the truth is that more important events took place while I was growing from one twentieth to one quarter of an inch in length than at any time since. And it is

only in embryos as small as this that we find the antique notochord in solitary occupation of the backbone site. Thereafter
it becomes rapidly replaced by harder and more complex materials: vertebral rings are laid down first as gristly cartilage,
then changed to harder bone. Apparently both in evolution
and in our own individual development a line is laid out, a
skeletal scaffolding built around it, and at last a hard resistant
material put in place.

In a sense, a fish stage exists for a time during the early development of every backboned animal now living on the land,
so long as we overlook the absence of the streamlined shape.
Most of what makes a fish a fish is there. Look first at the outside of a month-old human embryo. It could have been you
or me or anyone else. There is a head and neck region, a trunk
and a well-developed tail which tapers to a point. At this stage
the tail of a fish would be no better. There are two pairs of
lobe-like limbs and there is nothing to show whether they are
destined to be fins or arms and legs. While each side of the
neck shows several deep grooves which look exactly like those
which in a fish embryo would become gills. Even the heart is
much more fish-like than human at this stage, a two-cham-
bered heart that has already been pumping blood for two weeks
through embryonic gills.

This embryo of ours, when no longer than one eighth of an
inch, also possesses, as part of itself, an external yolk sac, a
water jacket, and an outgrowth corresponding to the waste
storage sac of a reptilian embryo. The yolk sac however is small
and quickly shrinks since it is empty of yolk from the beginning. The water jacket persists until birth and gives the embryo and prenatal baby both support and room to manoeuver
in, and its membrane rocks the baby as though in a cradle. It
is the caul which some of us are born with, though it is not
the sign of good luck it used to be thought, nor is it any longer
kept as a protection against drowning. These things belong

to an ancient reptilian past common to all mammals. The yolk sac is a relic and nothing more. The water jacket survives unchanged and carries on its original function of protection. But the third structure no longer stores liquid wastes, its walls are collapsed and the cavity has disappeared, and the lining and stalk serve as the placenta and cord which unite the embryo to the maternal tissues until the time of birth.

All of these are reptilian in origin and have been inherited by all mammals, but they also have been a living part of everyone of us. The fact that they have not persisted beyond my birth does not detract from the fact that they have been as integral a part of me as my milk teeth or the appendix that once was mine. I am less than human if I leave them out of my constitution.

Being a fish out of water however has its drawbacks. We are so wet inside that we splash when we fall from a high building on to a sidewalk. Yet it is a fact that under the dry hot conditions of the desert we would evaporate to death in a few hours unless counter-measures were taken. We are submerged in water for the first nine months of our existence, we are at least two-thirds water ourselves, and after we have been born we have an easily punctured and somewhat leaky skin between our inner wetness and the drying winds of the terrestrial earth. More than this, of course, we suffer from lack of the support of water.

The trouble begins when we are born. Until then a baby is supported comfortably by the liquid within the membranes and only the mother feels the weight of her burden. But once birth has occurred and the buoyant water has been replaced by insubstantial air, the infant is held down as though by a giant magnet wherever it is put. The body is too heavy for the limbs to raise and the neck muscles too weak to lift the head. And once we succeed, we grind along with our weight forever pressing on our feet or joints except when we stretch out or sit and spread. And the longer we live the more time there is for gravity to play havoc with our anatomy. For fifteen to twenty years we rise and shine. Thereafter time grows heavy and produces paunches and little bags below our eyes.

The sense of time is one of the greater mysteries, for the mind itself keeps time although not necessarily the same as the body, for states of mind affect one's estimation of it. Concentration on work in hand makes time pass one third faster than when idle; doubt and anxiety slow it down. Mental clocks keep time even in sleep as most of us know, and they run fast in fever. And like the flow of blood they run fast when young and slow down with age, so that the days of my youth were long days, while time rushes by as I get older and the mental seconds lengthen. Yet this may be as much the result of mind development as it is of a changing metabolic state. The more time we have experienced as individuals the longer is the yard stick by which we measure events or plan a project, and the more we become aware of self time, of memories of ourselves and anticipations of the future. We are a time-binding species and perhaps more than any other we have become a time-binding generation intent on reconstructing the past billion years and forecasting our planetary future. Which is why I am writing this, for it is a comprehension and an interest that increases as one grows older. In fact one of the great consolations life has to offer a mankind that is rapidly increasing in average age is that the process of aging affects the mind much less than the body. Minds get rusty more for lack of operation than for any basic deterioration in the equipment. In contrast to all other time-changes in the organism, mental potency as a whole rises sharply until the age of forty and continues to rise thereafter, although at a decreasing rate, until a climax is reached at about sixty. Then there is a slow decline through the next twenty years, though even at eighty the mental standard is still as good as it was at thirty-five. It is a different mind but no less valuable. And only an old pigmented brain produces that particular mixture of knowledge, experience and contemplation which is the reaction of intelligence to the changing circumstances of a long life. Wisdom, the highest product of the human mind, comes late; the young are rarely wise and are not expected to be. My own brain I am sure is as yet unpigmented, for neither my age nor my actions indicates sufficient wisdom. But 'the last of life, for which the first was made' is a line to remember, for the mind dominates in later years and grows only upon what it has been fed. How far it can fathom itself and the surrounding universe we have yet to learn.

2

TIME BINDERS

$\mathcal{T}$HE study of history, other than geneologies, is a surprisingly recent form of human behavior. Only for the last three centuries or so have individual human minds attempted to embrace the roaring onward sweeping confusion of events that comprise the human past as recorded in the written record. Yet the overwhelming detail and the fact that we are ourselves caught up in the stream make it difficult to discern the pattern and the trend, although the need to know what has happened and where we are drifting is becoming steadily if not desperately more important. There is clearly a momentum which is carrying us along, but what the course is can be shown I think only by extending the line of past events far beyond the inscriptions on stone and paper that have been left to us.

All the same, what is new is not so much the interest in the past as means employed to decipher it. Yet we have to go virtually to prehistoric times to find evidence of speculation as intense as our own. The remarkably evolutionary account of creation given in Genesis is in itself significant, although it appears to be derived in great part from the epics of creation of earlier Babylonian and Sumerian construction and to have been carried in the cultural baggage Abraham and his followers took with them when they emigrated from Ur. In any case it is somewhat chastening to find that the Sumerians of Mesopotamia, star watchers though they were, had put the age of mankind at 473,000 years, which is just about the figure now accepted. Even their estimation of the age of the earth at two million years is of an entirely different order from the biblical calendar of later times, although it is about one twentieth of what we at present believe it to be. Without any evidence of the kind we ourselves would regard as being in any way relevant, members of our species were brooding over the origin of the race five thousand years or more ago and somehow arrived at a reasonably correct estimation of its antiquity. The earth has filled up since then but we have gained neither in intelligence nor I think in wisdom. We have however had some further experience.

Reconstructing the past is a double exercise. We have to discover what has happened and also when the events took place. Just how fast is our headlong plunge into eternity and what kind of changelings are we? What sort of earthly spells have encompassed us? What light does it all throw upon the future?

Such are the problems. They are not new, but the last century and a half has vastly increased our appreciation of the nature of prehistoric events; while the last two or three decades have seen a remarkable exploitation of built-in time clocks both in rocks and in certain organisms. The very instability of matter which we call radioactivity not only holds the threat of extermination over our collective heads but can be induced to tell the age of fossils and minerals. It is a pity that war and the possibility of race suicide has so taken our attention that the greater significance of the atomic drama has been more or less overlooked. For it seems to me that the modeling of atomic matter by the mind, and its use to unravel time itself is a breath-taking episode in our small corner of the universe.

Atom bombs are based upon uranium but so are our measurements of the age of the earth. The principle involved is fairly simple. Radioactive elements are naturally disintegrating substances or they would not be radioactive. The uranium family, which are the heaviest, disintegrate with the liberation of radiation and helium gas, the parent substance passing step by step through a succession of intermediate stages of which radium is one until it finally settles down as a stable form of lead that is not radioactive. Since it is known at what rate each step is reached, the age of uranium-containing rock can be determined by estimating the relative amounts of uranium and lead which it contains. And since as a matter of fact most radioactive minerals contain three radioactive elements, two being forms of uranium and the other thorium, all producing lead at different rates and of distinguishable kinds, we can now get three independent determinations of age in one and the same mineral. If all three agree, assurance is rendered trebly sure, for, as it was with Joshua, what is said three times is true.

The rocks that contain these substances are found only here and there, which is a severe limitation, but they do serve to mark the salient points on our planetary time-scale. The oldest indicate ages of about 2000 million years, but as these are of rocks that are cut into older rocks which in turn record a long history, the age of the Earth must be considerably more than this. From three to four thousand million years is a generally accepted estimate. This gives us the over-all scale. Half or more than half of this is usually assigned for the period of evolution of life on the planet. A remarkable marine oil shale of Sweden which is of Cambrian age and contains some of the oldest kinds of fossils, turns out to be around 440 million years old; while what seem to be worm tracks in much older rock in Michigan appear to be more than twice as old. In terms of what you or I can comprehend with any real feeling there has been time verging on eternity for past existence of some sort. How much of it may be assigned to anything distinctively or even remotely human remains to be seen. There is one more date however which has been independently established, by the uranium-lead procedure, from localities in Norway and Bohemia with gratifying agreement. It places the end of early Permian time at 230 million years ago. It is a firm date and it marks the end of the great age of the coal forests and the beginning of the occupation of the land surface by four-legged backboned creatures who, each kind in its own time, have had their way with it ever since.

Two hundred or so million years is still too long a time to seize upon, although the first faltering quadrupedal step toward the warmblooded mammalian condition may have been taken as long ago as that. Fossil bones which are undoubtedly those of mammals that had a hairy coat and warm blood when alive appear in significant form in the rocks of the Tertiary epoch. Uranium dates rocks belonging to an early phase of this time at about sixty million years, although the dated samples do not mark the true beginning. The whole of the Age of Mammals must be reckoned to be a little longer, closer to seventy million years altogether. This is the age within which we must find ourselves. Somewhere between the beginning and the end our own kind came into being. But the uranium clock ticks too slowly to be of any further use and we need another measure. Unfortunately atomic clocks of another sort are lacking until we come close to the end and count years by the thousand instead of by the million.

The events and conditions of the past may be fascinating or to some of us perhaps no more than interesting, but I find a greater excitement in the process of discovery itself. There is a quality that is literally marvelous in the extraction of time from a mineral and in the reconstruction of a living past from rocky, oily, muddy, resinous or bony remains.

The age of mammals which saw us conceived and brought to our present imperfect state of fruition is long enough by all counts, too long in fact to be taken at one gulp. So for convenience and also because they do mark recognisable geological stages the period as a whole is subdivided into six smaller ones. They have their names, which might be worse: the Palaeocene or oldest age, the Eocene or dawn age, the Oligocene or the age of the few, the Miocene which should mean the middle age, the Pliocene which follows it, and the last and the least and by far the coldest, the Pleistocene. They are the six steps up which the various groups of mammals have climbed to their present status, and on one of them sits someone with the frankly curious and somewhat mischievous stare of an urchin or an ape.

Estimates of time based on thicknesses of the deposits constituting the various stages are hardly worth the paper they are written on, yet when we examine the rocks themselves to see what they may have to say concerning their own formation, we find they have a tale to tell.

Some stratified rocks show a thin layering like the rings in a tree, suggesting that each one may represent a year's deposit. They are known as varves, a Swedish term now in international use. The finest example of them all and the one showing the clearest indication of their annual nature is still the very first to have been recognized as such; it was described nearly a century ago—no time at all in terms of the scale we are examining but at least beyond the memory of any living man.

Certain shales of Miocene age in Switzerland bring that ancient world as vividly to life as any poster advertizing the glories of a Swiss canton. For layer upon layer repeat the following sequence: compressed in the bottom of each layer are the blossoms of poplar and camphor trees, symbols of spring; immediately above is a thin region containing winged ants and the seeds of elm and poplar, all of summertime; and this in turn is overlaid by the autumn fruits of camphor, date-plum and wild grape. The whole progression of the seasons, year after year, are there in the earth like an enchantment. Time past was as real as time present.

The varves most intensively studied are the potentially rich oil shales of Eocene age of the Green River in Wyoming and Colorado. The shales are very thinly layered, each layer consisting of two sheets of which one contains much more organic matter than the other. Together they represent a year's deposit, and the fact that they, like the rings in the trunk of a tree, vary in thickness in a cycle corresponding to the 11-year cycle of sun spots seems to confirm it. The Green River shales are 2,600 feet thick, the varves only about one two-hundredth of an inch, so that altogether they represent about six million years of accumulation. Green River time, which is one third of the Eocene, is the longest span so far measured directly from the rocks themselves. It gives us a yard stick of a substantial nature, although one so far little used.

Neither direct measurements nor radioactivity has so far given us much information concerning the durations of the Tertiary subdivisions. And in the end it is always with some feeling of incredulity that I face the fact that it takes the horse to tell us the time. Yet it is fitting after all, for we are more concerned with living time than any other kind, and the reason for so employing horses is that in layer after successive layer of the rocks from Eocene to Pleistocene the bones and skulls and teeth of horses lie scattered in amazing numbers. More is known of the character and rates of evolution of the various types of horses alive and dead than of any other kind of mammal. We may not be able to say exactly when man for instance was a half-recognisable sub-human, but we can say that when horses had reached such and such a stage, man was definitely a so and so. The little five-toed dawn horse, Eohippus of the Eocene, became the large one-toed modern horse, Equus of the Pleistocene, in the course of about sixty million years. The total period is that indicated by the geologic and radioactive evidence. But in between the beginning and the end Eohippus took its time to transform step by little step from a creature that looked rather like a dog to a superb runner of the steppes and prairies we have admired so much. Altogether nine genera of horses, each with its family of species, each more like a horse than the one before, bridged the expanse of Tertiary time; and this slow process of transformation in itself becomes the clock. So much evolution in so much time and we can apportion the millions we have to play with among the various periods according to how much went on in each. It gives us a neat little table:

Pleistocene	1 million years
Pliocene	11
Miocene	17
Oligocene	11
Eocene	20
Total	60

which will serve with reasonable accuracy as the calendar within which our own upstart evolution is to be found. I dare not leave you with the impression however that one little horse grew all alone into one big horse generation by generation. A whole crowd of small creatures that were already essentially horse in their basic constitution evolved successively into groups of larger and more obviously horsy types but differing among themselves at every stage. Most of these died out along the way. Eohippus was probably only one of several of the dawn horses, while Equus, which embraces our contemporary horse, ass and zebra together, is merely the lone survivor of the host that fell out by the wayside. If a three-toed, full-sized horse had also survived until the present we would be less inclined to look upon the horse evolution as a straight line drawn from the first to the last. What lives is no more than the tallest branch or twig. In their time the other branches were just as real.

There is a lesson in all of this which in an earlier day might have been driven home with a pointed finger and with righteous relish. It is important just the same. For what holds for horses applies to man. The genus Homo, and in particular the species selfnamed Homo sapiens, is the only one surviving. Therefore we say it was all meant to be so from the beginning. Yet if one of the other more or less human types which actually did survive until a few geological seconds ago had managed to come all the way as our companions, we would have to modify our views and probably much of our religion. As it is we still have a little trouble with the monkeys and the apes.

Time becomes more personal as we come closer to the present and I get a peculiar feeling when I realise that my own bones are dated. Probably they will survive me, for I cannot rely on being cremated when I am dead and it is all too likely I shall end up in a lead-lined coffin, which to my mind is a most improper use of valuable metal, let alone the energy expended in acquiring it, and is an even greater misuse of potential fertilizer—it brings to mind the parable of the man who had but one talent and buried it for safekeeping. All of us who promote this barbaric process of pickling the human dead and wrapping them in lead deprive nature of its right to claim its own dust. In the long run it will not be tolerated and nature will demand her own. Meanwhile the date of death can be read in the bones themselves long after a tombstone has weathered away.

The very air I breathe is radioactive, at least with regard to its carbon dioxide. We do not absorb this directly ourselves but all vegetation incorporates it and all that we eat contains carbon originally of atmospheric origin. Some of this is radioactive, having been bombarded by cosmic rays from outer space, although most is not; and while we live we keep the two in balance, since the general turn-over of carbon in the body is so rapid that in effect we always reflect the ratio of ordinary carbon and radioactive carbon present in the air and in the plants which are continually making use of it. But when we die no more is taken in and the radioactive carbon ticks away until all its radiation is gone and only the stable carbon remains. On a much shorter time scale it is the story of uranium and lead all over again—a built-in time clock in dead bone, or in wood for that matter, which runs down in thirty thousand years more or less, in place of the billion-year run of uranium. It serves well for dating organic remains through one of the most critical phases of human pre-history, although we urgently need other clocks that can tell us of past times over a much more extended range than carbon can, but in much more detail than we are told by uranium.

3

PATTERNS AND BONES

$\mathcal{T}$WO impulses tend to predominate whenever human beings encounter some tangible object new to their experience. Too often when it is alive the reaction is to shoot it. It is strange, it may be dangerous and so an element of fear arises; or if not fear, then the excitement of discovery must be pinned down as a trophy to exhibit to others. One way or another we are clearing the trash of creation out of our domestic landscape without even the excuse of not knowing what it is we do. The other means of escaping from strangeness is to give it a name, the more familiar the better. And so we classify and codify to our heart's content, noting differences and similarities and putting everything in its place, whether it be a flower, a bird or a man.

I can look upon a worm or a fish dispassionately, or even a jackass, but when I see a monkey I don't know whether to laugh or cry. There are differences to be sure but there is too much that is like me and I cannot build a fence that leaves monkey and myself upon the ground on separate sides; somehow I get the feeling that we are both sitting on the top rail, no doubt facing opposite ways but nevertheless perched up there together.

My hands and feet have five digits each, not unusual certainly and it would be disturbing to have them otherwise, but that is the point. It is the basic pattern of all four-footed animals and I share it not only with a monkey but with the mouse and the lizard, although many creatures have less than this, having lost some that they once possessed. I have seven vertebrae in my neck, like the monkey but also like the giraffe, the whale and the porcupine. I have four limbs, but so does a fish. In fact once we get rid of feelings we can make quite a game of matching bones and other things. The theory of evolution with its emotional overtones is an outcome of this practice rather than its instigator.

In principle it is no more complicated than matching counters. Like is put with like, the unlike are separated. The rest is sorted and arranged in place according to how much pattern or structure is shared, how much is different, and slowly the animal kingdom, particularly the backboned group which has had so much attention, assumes an intricate inter-relationship which is and can be subjected to no argument other than the place any one piece should occupy within the whole framework. It is simply a process of impartial observation and success depends upon acuity of vision of eye and mind. So it is that all reptiles are put into one class, birds into another and mammals in another again. Their bones and skulls, their whole skeleton, are so distinctively different there is no confusion whether a particular quadruped belongs in one category or another. Yet in spite of these distinctions they all exhibit so much structural similarity they clearly must be grouped together in a way that separates them from fish. And so it is that all mammals are clearly mammals no matter what view we may take as to their evolutionary origin. All those whose bones number and match in the same general way are mammals, and by no effort of the mind can I refuse to recognise that my skeleton is as typically mammalian as any, not to mention all my tissues and organs. That is my heritage and I am kin to all mammals in the first degree. And more remotely I relate to the rest of the vertebrated creatures, for the patterns are fundamentally the same and only the lesser features are strikingly different.

Within this class of mammalian types I naturally find my own niche, in the same manner as all the others. Limb, bones, the general skeleton, but above all teeth and skulls differ so that subdivisions are called for. There are many of them, some large and some small. Most of the huge horde of those that feed directly upon vegetation go into one, most of the flesh-eating carnivores into another; the chisel-teethed rodents have their own section, the whales a different one, and so on. We have our own, as long as we are willing to join those that belong there just as certainly. Otherwise there is no play, the game is off, and only chaos remains.

This orderly arrangement and subdivision of the animal kingdom was accomplished for the most part long before theories of evolution were put forward, although some such idea was implicit in the process. For classifying according to degrees of similarity and difference is itself a recognition of interrelationship, even though the relationships were no more than pattern in the mind of a creator. The concept of special creation, as though life in all its manifestations was the magical sprouting of a host of freshly sown seeds, long survived this classification. Even the discovery that fossilized animal remains frequently found embedded in the rocks were of different kinds from animals now alive failed to displace it.

The human mind, always ingenious and ready to solve a puzzle, the more easily the better, was not fazed: There was life on earth before the flood and the flood was simply the last of several world wide catastrophes during each of which all or almost all living things were destroyed and after which a new crop was sown. God's plaything in fact. Slowly however it dawned upon us, that is to say upon a few perceptive individual minds, that the dead animal forms in one layer of the rocks were in definite structural ways related to those above and below them, and the idea of a continuing transformation during the ages in place of successive and distinct replacements could not for long be withheld. A process of evolving was the simplest explanation that embraced all the known facts, and the concept of evolution continues to grow in strength because all the great mass of detail that keeps piling up eventually finds its place within the framework. There is nowhere else to put it. We have made a mental model of past and present life on this planet, as a natural inevitable, human intellectual exercise, and emotion enters only as we realise that we have to put ourselves into the same picture. And we do belong.

The study and interpretation of fossils is based upon an exceedingly obvious assumption, which is that in an undisturbed sequence of rock strata the lower of two layers is an older deposit then the one overlying it. In other words the succession of layers is a measure of time, with the oldest layer at the bottom and the most recent at the top. Hence the importance of knowing exactly where a fossil has been found, otherwise it is still lost in the fourth dimension.

The greater difficulties in reconstructing the past arise partly from the fact that the living forms of one period are in general the descendants of no more than a small part of those of a preceding one, for more fall by the wayside than continue along the road, and from the incompleteness of preservation of animal remains in fossil form.

Only skeletal remains as a rule persist long enough to become embedded, let alone mineralized, and in most cases no more than a few scattered parts survive to tell the story to those who may be able to read. All too often there is nothing but teeth, although these are more informative than any other single part of the body. In fact, when we attempt to trace mammalian fossil history all the way back, teeth, and tiny teeth at that, are virtually all that we find at the end of the trail, for enamelled teeth are far more resistant to decay than bone.

Given a more or less complete set of teeth, of one side of one jaw for instance, any zoologist should be able to identify its owner fairly closely. Mammalian teeth are clearly distinguishable from those of reptiles, and among the mammals each group has gone its own way, evolving grinders, cutters, slashers, chisels or even in some cases dispensing with them. Each kind reflects the special uses to which they have been put, the types of food and feeding habits, the size of the animal, and various other points. And when we examine the oldest fossil teeth and those of living mammals, other than the egg-laying and pouched relics of another sort, we are forced to conclude that the so-called insectivores are the most ancient and primitive. These are the shrews, hedgehogs and moles of our contemporary world, the least changed of the survivors of the earliest days of the age of mammals. They had and they have a total of forty-four teeth, compared with our thirty-two, of an effective type but not specialized for any limited purpose.

The problem that most fossils present is that of reconstructing the whole from a part, and it has all the fascination of reconstructing a crime from a bloody thumb print on the wall. In each case both the living and the dead have to be considered.

If fragments were all we had to work with I doubt if we could make much of them, but a living mammal is just as much a mammal as one that has been dead fifty or sixty million years. It may be different in size, in body proportions, and in almost every detail, but it is built according to the same basic blueprint. There are the same number and kinds of bones in the skull, for instance, each joined to its neighbors by sutures, and given one or two adjoining pieces each can be recognized for what it is. And inasmuch as skulls vary in shape and size as a whole, the configuration of a part dictates the plan for the rest. And from a thigh bone we can build up the rest of the leg, determine how much weight it carries and how the body is moved, but only because we can study the general relation of bones to muscles and work to be performed in animals now alive. In the light of this every piece of bone has something to say. It has grooves, ridges, rough places, indentations or bumps, thickness and shape, all of which reflect the attachment of muscles and tendons, the mass of adjacent tissue, the stresses and strains it has been subjected to, for no matter how hard a skeleton may be, it is or has been truly alive and has been molded according to the circumstances of the growing animal and its activities. Evoking the living flesh from a dead scrap is a fine art certainly, but it is an entrancing if laborious occupation, and sooner or later something else usually turns up which either confirms or modifies the predicted whole.

No animal lives alone, whether it be human, subhuman or otherwise. It has companions and a world to live in, and you can no more abstract a creature from its way of life than we can make sense out of placing man in outer space. We are all earthlings. And so climate, vegetation, predators, and everything that constitutes the circumstances of a life are as important to recapture as the nature of the sensate being enveloped by them. They belong together as closely as a river to its bed.

4

CLIMBERS

SOMEWHERE in this interminable earthly history we must find a starting point. To go back to the beginning of the planet or of life is too far and involves too much. We have to take our mammal for granted it seems to me and begin with the oldest and in a general way the most primitive of them, though the same point of departure might as well be taken for the trail leading to cows and cats in place of human beings. For long ago, even before Tertiary time, when the age of reptiles was declining although far from over, small placental mammals were abundant, judging from the multitude of tiny teeth, fragments of jaws, not to mention a few skulls, that lie scattered across the earth. As far as we can tell from these remains they were remarkably like the shrews of our present time, so much so in fact that I doubt whether we can point to any notable feature in a shrew's body and manner of living and say with certainty that it has changed from what it used to be, except perhaps that their bite is now poisonous. To take a living creature however and regard it as the living unchanged embodiment of an ancient past is a dangerous procedure and is usually frowned upon. For if a small animal that resembled a shrew has been able in the course of sixty or seventy million years to evolve into a man, can we reasonably expect that any similar creature could have persisted throughout so long a time without changing in a marked degree? In spite of this possible pitfall I believe that we can see in the modern shrews something of the world and the life from which our kind has taken its origin. They seem to me to fulfill everything I have been led to think that ancient stock to have been, and on this assumption we can find our most distant mammalian relatives in the nearest patch of woods, living out their short lives in the olden manner almost in our own backyard.

I have rarely seen a shrew, although they are common. But for one long summer at the edge of a forest of spruce, oak and birch, several of them, perhaps a family, rushed around in their own small circuits, while I moved more slowly among them in mine. You had to look twice, if there was time enough, to make sure that what you saw was not a mouse, although the resemblance apart from size and speed is only superficial. A small black streak, often followed by another, and it was gone—with elfin shrieks sometimes issuing from a nearby pile of leaves. Yet nothing I have ever seen has seemed so vital. If such were our beginnings it is no wonder the force of life is so far from being spent.

Three inches long, it is as ferocious as a small tiger, though that is an understatement for no large mammal could possibly live at the pace of a shrew and none could be so fierce. If this is the way it used to be it was not the meek who inherited the earth but an intense, all-consuming furnace contained within small furry bodies. Only short interludes of family life interrupt an incessant, high-pitched career of eating and fighting. All is energy and action and the fuel to maintain it. Possibly the most highstrung of all animals, the shrew's every movement is quick and jerky, accompanied by a twittering series of short high pitched squeaks. Even in the rare moments when it is standing still its nose is working and sniffing, and its tiny ears are seemingly strained for the slightest sound, for it sees none too well.

Until I met the shrew I thought that humans had the greatest catholicity of taste of any living creature, but shrews outdo us. They live up to their class name of insectivore and go far beyond it. Beetles, butterflies, crickets, hoppers, ants, and grubs and centipedes are gulped down as fast as they can be caught. Slugs, snails and earthworms are taken just as fast, and so are mice if they are slow in moving out of the way. Their own weight in meat every three hours is the pace desired, although if meat is scarce they turn to berries, nuts and coniferous seeds. Like a man or a bear a shrew is omnivorous.

Shrew life is short and fast, though far from merry. If not cut off by an owl or hawk or weasel it ends in a sudden senility, a quenching of the blazing little flame, after about fifteen months. Once around the sun, two or three families produced within a leafy nest beneath a log, too much eaten much too fast, and it is over. Prolific, insatiable, poor-sighted and color-blind, with a probing snout and short legs, a shrew above all is of the earth earthy, a creature of the ground, living in the semi-dark of logs and leaves and underground spaces, in a world of low-down smells and sudden swooping danger. Is this where we start? I believe so.

It seems a somewhat inauspicious beginning, apart from the living intensity. Yet all that makes a mammal is there, in heart, brain and body, not to mention milk glands and a litter of offspring conceived and nourished within the womb, a mammalian combination that has been the key to success. But alongside this is the diminutive size, short life, weak sight and predominating sense of smell. And still the assets and the liabilities go together and reflect the conditions of life when the mammal itself was in the making. For the land in those distant days was overrun by reptiles, gigantic and otherwise, and in order to survive and reproduce, the early stock of hairy, warm-blooded creatures had to keep to secret ways or to the dark, had to eat whatever could be found, and had to carry their developing young within them rather than lay eggs where they could too easily be discovered. They were on the run, driven more or less underground or to foraging at dusk or through the night—a desperate kind of life that demanded a high fertility and a quick replacement of generations. Nothing like it had been seen before, for life reached a new high level of energy, withal subdivided into multitudinous multiplicative little individual fragments that could never be stamped out altogether. But compared with the reptilian past from which they emerged, noses and the sense of smell became all-important, while eyes degenerated during the dim ways of the many million years. No matter what you may see in a sunset or in a flower, all the evidence indicates that mammals as a whole are color-blind and have been so from their beginning. They belong to the semi-dark in a world that was already commencing to take on a familiar look, when the monotonous coniferous forests of the reptilian age were becoming mixed with walnut, beech, tamarisk, plane and laurel, as well as juniper, pine and sequoia. Vegetation was subtropical, wide-spread and uniform, from the equator to the poles. It is in a setting such as this that we start to climb our tree, and the way of a shrew takes us to its roots.

It was Chesterton who wrote "goodness only knowses the Noselessness of Man," though I doubt that he realized how much lay behind it. We still have a sense of smell to be sure, enough to appreciate jasmine or a rose and to dislike the odors in city smog; but little enough compared with most of our mammalian colleagues. And thereby hangs the tale, for odors have enslaved virtually all those who have kept their nose and their feet close to the ground. The scent of their own or of other kinds have more urgent meaning for these than anything to be heard or seen, fraught with bonds or danger or even ecstasy. We miss a lot certainly—"the smell of dew and thunder, of old bones buried under," but we have gained the rainbow and the setting sun.

Man, in his distinctively human form, has so recently appeared, biologically speaking, that it is disconcerting to have to go so far back into time to find the first tentative steps that were taken away from the general run of the mammalian mill. Shrew-like animals must have taken to an arboreal life as soon as the new diversity of trees came into being, animals that were remarkably like the tree-shrews now living in the Indonesian forests. For almost at the very beginning of Tertiary time, even before the Eocene dawn, most of the mammalian pathways had already been chosen. And tree life offered several opportunities.

Think for a moment what it means to climb a tree. You have to watch what you are doing, and whether or not there is anything to smell, your nose is definitely unemployed. Above all you use your hands. The change from grubbing along the ground to clambering among the branches swung the evolution of little insectivorous mammals in the human direction; although the path was also open to other ways, for it led to bats as well as monkeys and their kind.

I am fully aware that bats lie outside the line of our ancestry but they have a fascination and a peculiar interest all the same. Bats and human beings are the only mammals that truly fly, and bats do it without the help of mechanical aids. More than that, bats were bats as far back as the Eocene, sixty million years ago. They have changed little since that time for the reason that the requirements for flight are so rigid that once an organism has become perfected for it, it cannot change significantly and retain its state of perfection. Yet here is the point, which brings me and a bat to a closer understanding.

Bats are without doubt the direct descendents of the shrewish mammals that first climbed into the trees, whose fore-feet spread out into grasping hands, stretching skin from the sides of the body as planes for gliding from branch to branch, finally launching into space as the most proficient flying acrobats this earth has ever seen—taking off from the tips of branches and flying with their fingers. Their path led from the ground straight up into the sky. In the evolutionary sense of long ago these were my brothers, for I grew out of those who also found the trees but who failed to fly until after I myself was born.

The world that bats evolved in however was richly forested and it was not necessary to leap into space to obtain the insects the shrew folk had become accustomed to eat. Tree buds, seeds and fruit, birds' eggs and nestlings, slow-moving insects and their slower grubs were there for the taking, and throughout the early phases of the Tertiary, through Palaeocene and Eocene, a certain arboreal type for which the only name is tarsioid lived in abundance over most of the earth. One lone relic survives to show us how its bones were fleshed and how its life was lived: the Spectral Tarsier of the Indonesian jungle. It is a primate, like ourselves, though at the other end of the scale.

You can hold a tarsier upon the palm of your hand like a Tom Thumb, and like a manikin it might stare back at you with both of its large round eyes focussed on your face. Even if its body were turned away it can still look at you, not by swinging its eyes sideways the way you look at someone passing you on the street but by pivoting the head as a whole, even to the extent of looking straight backwards over its shoulders; for the eyes are fixed in their sockets in an owl-like stare and are so large that the face seems flattened, so little of the snout protrudes. The ancient tarsiods were apparently much the same, except that they were not so agile jumpers, for the specter's hind legs are lengthened and it can leap distances its

ancestors could not, although the peculiar eyes and the necessity to jump from branch to branch are intimately connected.
The importance of this is easily shown if you are ready to make
the unwise experiment of jumping across a ditch with one
eye closed. Sure enough you will either fall short or overreach
and had it been a branch of a tree instead of the edge of a ditch
either mistake could cost you your life. So it has been for the
Spectral Tarsier and its relatives throughout past and present
time. Two eyes directed forwards are needed for binocular
vision; eyes at the side of the head afford a panoramic vision
but are of little use for estimating distance and it is for this
purpose that the eyes of the Tarsier face the front. And why
ours do also. Yet in certain ways the Tarsier eyes are intermediate between those of mammals in general and those of
monkeys, apes and men. The old-fashioned, side-placed eyes
gave separate images and could be moved in their sockets
independently of each other, although predatory animals have
their eyes much more to the front than those they chase. The
Tarsiers needed to move the pair together, focussed on the same
object, in order to get some sense of distance, but they could
not manage the synchronized control except by fixing the eyes
and rotating the head as a whole.

In ascending the trees and living among the branches the
third dimension of space and the one most involved with the
force of gravity, was added to existence. And it became as
necessary to truly sense the third dimension as it was unnecessary in the flat land life of an older time. Bats developed
hearing to its utmost pitch for estimating distance by means of
sound; tarsiers peeked round two sides at once with a pair of
eyes and saw space instead. And the brain of the tarsier shows
it. The visual areas of the cortex at the back of the brain are
enormously enlarged compared with those of a shrew; while
the olfactory region for smell is shrunk, together with the
snout, two changes that become more and more pronounced as

we proceed. They set limits to a mind and form to a face.

The tarsier survives almost unchanged since the Eocene age of sixty million years ago. That is so long ago its antiquity is hard to feel, although it can be measured. Yet it holds a warning, for it shows that life does not necessarily go on evolving. The tarsier came to a standstill while it was still as color-blind as its mammalian forbears, though with eyes enlarged to see better in the dark. Most of its closest relatives have long since disappeared. Some of them did survive however, only not as tarsiers, and we are among those who live to tell the tale. But it is a curious tale in so many ways, and one of these is brought home to me every time I have seen a South American monkey.

Unless our brains are more twisted than we think, the monkey has happened twice. I find it difficult to believe, having looked long at monkeys of both the Old World and the New, but it is as simple as arithmetic and the answer just as definite. In Eocene times, when the nearest thing to monkey kind were the little tarsiers scattered over the world, the continent of South America became detached from the north. For almost the whole of subsequent time the Central American bridge has been absent and there has been no way for the monkey tribes to enter the southern continent, nor apparently have there been any such folk in North America waiting to make the jump. The conclusion seems inescapable that the tarsiers in South America and in the combined continents of Asia and Africa have independently progressed to monkey status. If there has been time for one there has been time for both—that is not the problem. The problem is one of choice. Either monkeys managed to cross long stretches of ocean from the old world continent without any plausible means of doing so, or what seems to be monkey has evolved in each location. Even continental bridges across the Atlantic, since sunken, have been evoked to solve the dilemma, which is like raising the devil to fight a fire. It is easier in the end to face the facts and say that there were tarsiers here and tarsiers there; now there are monkeys here and monkeys there; and that tarsiers became monkeys in both places. From a similar start and under similar circumstances evolution is likely to proceed along parallel lines. The Old World monkeys sitting on their tails and the New World monkeys swinging from theirs is an image repeated with but minor differences. I believe it did happen this way in the course of primate evolution and it raises the thought that what happened at an early stage for monkey might have happened later on for man. For the question has been put whether or not we are all of one origin. The answer must be deferred.

Whether we as human beings are willing to admit apes or monkeys into our ancestry is somewhat beside the point. A rose by any other name is just as sweet and somewhere in our past in the Oligocene age a creature lived that was more than a tarsioid and was in some ways less than any monkey or ape now alive, and very much less than a man. Yet it was fully arboreal and much better perfected for that kind of life than any of its own ancestors. We might just as well call it monkey and be done with it, though without prejudice as to the length of its tail.

I do not believe we can possibly overestimate the importance of arboreal life in our evolutionary upbringing. I cannot conceive how anything remotely like a human could have evolved in any other way, for the ground holds its creatures in mental and physical chains, shackling the senses and demanding that feet be used for running. We are not so free ourselves but we are at least partly emancipated, and such freedom as we have traces directly back to a tree-top life.

Consider what it means! It is more than the fact that vision increases in value and that feet convert into a kind designed for grasping boughs and branches. It is the combination and interaction of these, together with some other tree-born changes. And any monkey will serve as illustration. The tarsiers merely led the way.

To begin with there is increase in size, a change that is always significant no matter what sort of animal we are contemplating; for it is impossible to grow larger and remain exactly the same in other ways, whatever appearances may seem to show. Increased weight puts greater demands upon the climbing mechanism and both the fore and hind feet of monkeys and apes have responded by becoming grasping organs, with opposable thumbs or big toes according to how you wish to look on them. Pairs of grasping hands and feet are as definitely an outcome of climbing trees as is the degeneration of the sense of smell. First and foremost they are adaptations for the peculiar kind of locomotion required for running along branches of various thicknesses. This mode of life, especially in association with the increased body weight, places a heavy survival value upon balance and upon accuracy in judging distances to be jumped between one branch and another, much more than for the timid and lighter tarsiers.

Senses and brain have developed accordingly. The sensations for balance streaming both from the labyrinth of the inner ear and from all the muscles and tendons of the body are cleared in a correspondingly enlarged region of the brain. While sight is infinitely enhanced; eyes are more accurately aligned to the front, are movable and their movements exactly coordinated; binocular vision has become more stereoscopic, with the visual cortex of the brain enormously increased. You can almost see how it has come about. For generation after untold generation those individuals who lost their balance or misjudged a distance, particularly when very young, fell fatally or were injured and played no part in reproducing the race. Propagation was left to those with better eyes and better balance, and the inexorable selection of such as these year in and year out for ten million years or so made the monkey what it is. And inasmuch as propagating in the tree tops is a precarious procedure for relatively heavy creatures, births become limited to a single one in place of litters, even at the tarsier stage. One offspring at a time is the rule when the mother runs and jumps among the branches and the baby has to hang on to her for its life.

Such are the fundamentals, the basic conditions for survival. Where do they lead? For one thing they lead to hands. It is easier and probably safer, when resting in a tree, to sit rather than lie down. It is safer and more proficient to reach out for an insect with a grasping appendage than to stretch your neck and use your jaws. When sitting or when moving but slowly about in search of food, two or three holdfasts are enough, leaving one or two free for other purposes. Sitting upright upon a branch not only gave rise to hands but started the trend toward an upright body. To be able to pick up and clutch a locust was simply an extension of the ability to hold on to a slender branch with four fingers and an opposable thumb. Almost inadvertently the primitive mammalian foot became transformed into a multipurpose tool-like hand, although its use depended greatly on changes in the eyes.

The improvements which the monkey eye developed are exactly those that we make the most use of, though we take them much too much for granted. For when we consider that our most remote mammalian ancestors were with little doubt both weak-sighted and color blind, it seems to me almost miraculous that we should be able to see in certain ways better than any other kind of mammal with the exception of our poor relations. The improvements are three-fold and we owe them to our predecessors who lived out their lives in the colorful and blazing light in the uppermost layer of tropical forests. Flowers, buds, insects, birds' eggs and the birds themselves all contributed to a riot of color unknown on the ground below, and most of them were good to eat. And it was only natural to hold in front of your eyes for a moment what you were about to eat, to record its image for future reference. Yet somehow out of such a practice color vision has become resurrected in an eye which had lost it. Convergent eye movements which were necessary to bring into combined focus a close-up object conveyed an impression of depth and solidity. And the small central area of the retina of each eye became infinitely complex for registering the greatest detail. Three-dimensional color vision of marvelous acuity came from feeding on everything in sight in a colorful immediate world. Sight became dominant above all else and left us with windows opening on the universe.

The eye and the hand. They make most of a monkey and much of a man, for they work together. Large areas develop in the brain not merely for the sensations of light and touch but for the memories of past sensations also. The brain evolved great storage places for the past, of solid things with color and texture. Eyes do more than look at an object. With imperceptible movements they caress the outlines in three dimension and make a record of solid shapes. In a more obvious manner the fingers do the same—and for a creature's own body as well as things external to it. Between the two there comes a physical awareness of self and an ardent curiosity, from exploring with fingers and exploring with eyes. This also is our heritage, but it also goes back to our simian past in the early Oligocene. And so does the first great expansion of the frontal part of the brain, those lobes concerned with planning and the future in contrast to the sensory and memory regions that represent the present and the past. Our brains have expanded and improved since that distant time, but the kind of brain we have is essentially still the same—a brain that glories in sight; is avid for touch, appreciates sound; and knows hardly any smell. It is a special kind of brain with potentials and limitations that were set some forty or fifty million years ago. The more we know of it the better, for it shapes our destiny.

5

SITTERS

ONE of the most striking qualities of human beings, so far as I can see, is the alacrity with which we sit down whenever the occasion offers. I have found it a great relief ever since I can remember and properly cultivated it should lead to a more enjoyable old age, if not a longer life. We appear to be the world's best sitters and I know of nothing more illustrative than the atavistic self-assignment of sitting for days on end on the top of a flagpole that was a craze a little while ago. We ride to work or play sitting in cars or in trains as though legs were unheard of. A sign of modern degeneracy? Not exactly. We have had a squatting or sitting career that may well be as old as our thumbs, lasting for several tens of millions of years. There were times when we sat upright upon our ends more assiduously than at other times, and times when legs came more into their own as a means for getting places. Yet altogether the impress has been extensive, spreading all the way from local wear and tear to a tired neck.

Gravity is no idle force, and whether we stand up or just sit up the effect upon our bodies is much the same. In four-legged creatures the body is slung like a hammock between four posts, with the various internal organs and the long digestive tube partly suspended by ligaments from the upper side and partly supported by the horizontal body wall below. Stand the same kind of body upright, whether hanging by its arms, standing on its legs, or poised upon its rear, and the stomach and intestine no longer hang straight down from the backbone as they did but sag parallel with it; while the supporting ligament itself has a smaller and less secure hold on the backbone. More than this, the heavy abdominal viscera thrust against the weak wall of the lower abdomen incline it to rupture and lessen the flow of blood from the legs to the body. Waist muscles have to hold the body erect which previously were called upon for little effort. Even heart and kidneys tend to dangle, as they do most disturbingly in persons excessively thin. And that gone feeling which often comes when midnight is long since past and you are still up and about is simply the sagging of the inner man as gravity wins the final round. All are penalties for being up-ended, but as sitters, not as walkers. They raise the question of a tail.

The devil is usually pictured with a tail. Whether this has any connection with our obvious reluctance to admit a monkey into our family circle I do not know. Do we abhor a tail because our lack of it appears to be our greatest distinction, the only clear cut difference between us and our more hairy companions? If so then we still have company whether we like it or not. And in the end the question is not how we lost a tail but what have we done with it? We sit on it, and so do the apes on theirs for the same reason and from the same heritage!

On all anatomical grounds these are our kin and this matter of a tail is as good a case in point as any. The tail in an ape and a man is not lost but hidden. It is short, certainly, but we have one just the same and employ it, especially its muscles, to form a floor for the pelvic region for the greater support of our abdominal organs now pressing against our lower end. Those muscles which in a frightened dog depress the tail and give the animal some moral if not physical support become spread out to form the pelvic floor, with the bony column inevitably brought in as part of the equipment. Having changed our base we had to build another platform and the whole process of conversion is clearly seen during the growth of the young embryos of apes and humans.

There are only four kinds of living apes if we exclude the more elegant type commonly known as man: the comparatively primitive gibbon of southeast Asia and our three friends, the chimpanzee Pan, the orang-utan Pongo, and Gorilla the gorilla. The first and last of these are African, while the orang-utan lives in the same forests as the gibbon.

The present interest started with Pongo, for orang-utans were the first apes to be brought back in captivity to Europe, late in the seventeenth century, and their living presence started men thinking. In fact one of the awkward habits of the mind is that, consciously or otherwise, it goes on thinking about what it has seen and heard in an uncontrollable attempt to make it all fit together. Asleep or awake the process continues and often enough the conscious mind is only aware of the resulting conclusions, like the voices heard by Joan of Arc. When properly harnessed it becomes the most powerful force we know.

The more or less human quality of the orang-utan was recognized from the beginning, to a greater extent in fact than was actually justified, for legend gave these ape-men of the forest a much higher intelligence than they really possessed, while the truly human hottentots with which they were compared were grossly underrated. The outcome however was to blur any line that might have been clearly drawn between human beings and less human creatures, and a century later theories of evolution began to sprout in the humid and fertile soil of the minds of certain men. Now, a century or so later again, we seek for the fossilized bones of apes with an anticipation exceeded only by the hope of finding remains that are neither fully ape nor fully human. And the oldest recognized fragments of ape belong to one that was little more than twenty inches in height, the length of a newborn human baby, which lived in early Oligocene time—no antique piece of purely monkey so far found is any older. Sitting upright upon our hidden tail has been a practice for longer than we thought.

Taking all the evidence together, all that is known of fossil apes and all that is known of the living, ape evolution has been a two stage affair, one represented by the lightweight gibbons and the little fossil apes and the other by the giant primates among whom we find or should find our place. We can look at them in this order, for either from the small tree-ape stage or from the later giant ape group we took our departure along a path of our own. In either case the small gibbon-like apes of the Oligocene are antecedent to the rest and ancestral to them, and the present day gibbons are the least changed of their descendents.

Of all four kinds of undiluted apes now living the gibbons are the most thoroughly arboreal and they differ from the ancient forms mainly in being somewhat larger, about three feet from head to heel, with very greatly elongated arms and moderately lengthened legs; and longer canine teeth. Apart from the more weapon-like teeth the changes are simply those which have made the living gibbons more proficient arboreal acrobats than their ancestors. They have become better constructed for running along boughs and for swinging from branch to branch, two activities that other apes and man can perform remarkably well considering their size and weight, although by no means so well as a gibbon. We all acquired the skills during our common tree-ape status in Oligocene time and our bones show it. We can see it in the gibbon, although gibbons take even less kindly to captivity than the other apes and they are not readily studied in the tree tops by their more sophisticated relatives. They have been studied all the same but any gymnasium will show you most of it, for it is all too clear that we have not only remembered our habits of long ago, but revel in their practice. How else can we account for our youthful passion for trapeze work, except as a nostalgic substitute for the long-lost boughs and branches? Bodies require exercise along the lines for which they are made and it is quite obvious that our hands and arms in particular are perfectly designed for swinging hand over hand along overhanging bars or ropes or branches. Except for the slow-motion sloth no one but a man and an ape can do it; and a man does it only a little less well than an ape and far better than monkeys.

Arm locomotion, common to all the apes, involves the suspension of the body with its spine perpendicular to the ground, and an extreme mobility of the fore limb is required. Hang on to a bar or a branch for a moment with one arm and you will appreciate it better. You can grasp the bar firmly and yet be able to twist and turn as the bones of your fore-arm and wrist rotate, while the bone of your upper arm swivels in its shoulder socket almost as well as a universal joint. These are freedoms of movement perfected primarily for a gibbon-like life. And the stresses involved have brought in their train other changes such as a broadening and flattening of the chest, a strengthening of the collar bones, and an increase in the use of the diaphragm for breathing to compensate for the weakening of the chest muscles. A shortening of the distance between our ribs and our sacro-iliac and the balancing of the skull upon its atlas appear to be part of the same general shift. The rigidity of the collar bone is as essential for this free-swinging locomotion as it is an impedance for those that run on all fours with a springing step, such as a horse or leopard; in such as these the collar bone has gone, for the same reason that when we fall heavily upon our hands our own collar bones break. Skeletons, like teeth, tell their own story. Man's missing ribs, for there is little doubt that we have lost a pair, disappeared from another cause more related to walking than swinging. It had nothing to do with Eve.

Life amidst the crowns of trees in tropical forests must have been, as it still must be, a pleasant contrast to the life most mammals lead on the ground below. Color came back again, which must have enriched the mental world whatever meaning it may have possessed; while to a great extent fear has gone. Predators no longer lie in wait as they do for most of the earth-bound creatures whose dominant emotion is a nervous apprehension. In the trees all is changed except for the presence of certain snakes and the greatest danger lies in a faulty balance or a misplaced jump. Even at this distance nothing terrifies a child or a man as much as the sensation of falling into space. Trees tend to keep their folk in trim just as definitely as the air dictates the shape of an air-borne bird. Size, form and skill must be maintained.

Security, a wide variety of food, and a lively colorful environment comprised an arboreal Eden, and if the fall of man has any evolutionary meaning, this is the place we fell from. At least it is the place where our love-life and our particular process of propagation were first established.

Primate reproduction is distinctive, whether it be human, ape or monkey. Almost everything is different in certain definite ways, and it is hard to avoid the conclusion that these differences are the outcome of the arboreal adventure. A Frenchman has said "that which distinguishes a man from the beast is drinking without being thirsty and making love at all seasons," which is clearly true with regard to drink but is only true for the other when we lump monkey, ape and man together. For all three of us the limited breeding season, so typical of the animal world in general, has gone and we all produce our young at any time of the year. It speaks well for the arboreal environment and for the one human beings have manufactured as a substitute; for breeding seasons are imposed by the conditions into which a babe is born, which must be conducive to survival. All else is adjusted to this, and the lack of any particular season for birth implies that all seasons are good. The pattern was set in the tropics, although in the more extensive tropics of an age long past—or it might be better to say that the older seasonal restraints were lifted, and just as apes and monkeys can lift their voices freely without fear of retribution they have become free to breed at any time without untoward consequences to their offspring. Whether moonlight set the rhythm of the monthly period of ovulation in our early arboreal ancestors is hard to say, but it is possible that the night and the moon and you is a very old refrain which carries us back to the tops of the trees.

So do a few other items in our repertoire, for the tree-top communities lived in a world that was virtually their own, a world that gibbons and monkeys still possess. The greater apes have slipped a little. Social groups of various size and kind are to be found, from large clans of monkeys to the small monogamous family of the gibbon. But whether large or small, certain needs and opportunities arise which are more restricted when on the ground. When senses are no longer continually alerted to the possible presence of enemies they can be used more often for other functions, and perhaps for the first time a sense of luxury develops. Many creatures groom themselves it is true but mutual grooming among grown adults I believe is confined to the higher primates. Idle minutes or even hours are spent on careful examination and cleaning of the hairy coat since hands and eyes both need work to do. And the general principle of you scratch my back and I'll scratch yours must be traced to the new-found leisure in the seclusion of a tree; and so perhaps the one concerning idle hands and mischief-making. So much that we think is purely human we have to share with those who look most like us, including a certain tendency to be vulgar.

Social groups in an arboreal world have their own particular problems. Individuals or neighboring groups may be close enough together or even much too close and yet be out of sight. So voices are raised as a means of signalling to those unseen, with varying import. On the other hand the pathways and resting places among the trees are inevitably narrow and restricted. Individuals of a group are forever coming face to face and a certain mutual understanding of intentions is essential if the cohesion within a group is to be stronger than the disruptive force of irritation. Sound is not necessary for such close-up communication and mobile mouths and faces are only too expressive. We flatter ourselves when we say that only man can speak. Both vocal and silent kinds of speech are used by apes and monkeys, the first mainly for coordinating a social group or communicating with another, the other more for communication between two individuals. Combine them, the movements of tongue, lips and facial muscles with the production of sounds, and we have true speech. Apes are limited in their use of it but so are we. And both in the case of a gibbon and a man the voice is often raised when there is no call for it, in sheer exuberance in a morning shower, whether it be in a bathroom or a tree top. Our spirits rose when we climbed our tree. They have been soaring ever since and often beyond all reason.

6

WALKERS

You can generally tell a man by his gait, although watching my fellow beings walking down the street I have often wondered. It is all too easy to see the limb of a tree in place of the city sidewalk, and the slight but rhythmic swaying from side to side becomes highly suggestive. We follow a narrow line, though sometimes with a disconcerting difficulty; and in our younger years at least walk joyfully and unselfconsciously along the edge of a curb or the top of a wall. Walking on two legs is one of the finer arts and an exhilarating one before the mechanism begins to wear, but it is not ours alone.

Walking with our hind legs only, when you come to think of it, is a double feat. It consists of balancing upright and teetering along without falling on our face, as though walking on stilts, and it is a process of clutching and levering along the ground with our chronically flattened feet. Men and apes are both good walkers each in his own way, but his own way is for walking in different places. The ape walk came first, which is where we start, and it is curious I think that bipedal walking in its original form was acquired less for any merit of its own than as a consequence of using the arms for brachiation, the hand and the arm-swinging method of locomotion along the underside of overhead branches, with legs and feet reaching for and occasionally running along branches below. The gibbon is again the best living illustration for on the infrequent occasions when it leaves the trees for the ground it walks more erect and more like a man than do any of the other apes inasmuch as it is the least top heavy, and still it is the greatest trapeze artist of us all. Long swinging leaps from tree to tree may carry the animal anywhere from thirty to fifty feet, although the excessively lengthened arms used in this performance appears to be a gibbon's own speciality. The rest of us have stopped more or less short along this particular road. Yet the very use of the arms for locomotion in this way virtually forced the legs into the business of alone supporting the body from below, somewhat in the manner that a waiter carries a tray through a crowded restaurant. After all, carrying the body load poised alternately on the top of one thigh bone and the other has required a lot of practice. It is a skill that has been exploited at first among the trees, for frequent hand holds are almost a necessity for any prolonged progression of this kind. This is true not only of the gibbon and other apes, for we see something very close to it every time an infant learns to stand and walk. There is a period when faltering steps are only possible as long as the arms can reach out for a bar or a helping hand; this much at least belongs to our arboreal past. The more difficult question is at what stage in our history did we abandon tree life and take to our more independent and unsupported ways upon the ground.

Two or three possibilities exist, each favored by one authority or another, although all regard biological man as essentially ape. The only difference of opinion concerns the point of divergence and there is no comfort here for those who desire to exclude the ape altogether, for in the sense that beggars disagree there is no disagreement at all.

So that what we have to decide is whether we as prospective humans struck off on our own when our arboreal ancestors were still more or less four-footed like the more primitive monkeys, whether we did so during the light-weight, short-bodied gibbon stage, or whether we waited until we were already in the great ape stage from which gorillas, orang-utans and chimpanzees also have descended. In various details of bony structure man and gorilla have more in common than man has with any other kind, and we can only conclude that either we are closely related to the most disagreeable of the apes or else that much of the similarity is a result of parallel evolution. It is a choice that confronts us all along—has there been but one path to a certain end or have two paths run side by side?

The first possibility is the least likely. Monkeys are not so fully adapted for tree locomotion as apes and the only truly grounded monkeys at the present time are the baboons who have become less, not more, bipedal, so much so that at a distance they look like dogs, although they retain an advanced monkey brain and a vivid physical expression of color. It is most unlikely that such as these, but more insignificant in size, ran along the ground on all fours, as one anthropologist has put it, until they got their hands so filled with food, weapons, or mischief that they had to stand up and walk on their hind legs.

The decision in fact lies between the gibbon and the larger apes as representatives of the lithe, primitive apes of the late Oligocene and the heavier, tree-squatting apes of the succeeding Miocene period, between a splitting from the arboreal stock some thirty odd million years ago or at a time perhaps ten million years later on. One could say, when speaking of time in such dimensions, that it makes no odds, but that would not be true for it is time itself that sets us in our ways and trims the mind to certain channels. All the fossil record actually tells us is that up to the end of the Oligocene period only gibbon-like apes were present and that in the Miocene which followed the so-called giant apes were on the scene, diversifying rapidly into many types. And we have need to remember that the gibbon itself and the other three living apes are our contemporaries, and have therefore persisted through time as more or less arboreal creatures for a score or more million years since our human ancestors came down to earth. Gibbon ape and giant ape are no longer what they used to be. The smaller size of the gibbon left it plenty of space to swing in, an opportunity fully exploited, and now a gibbon's arms are so long its hands touch the ground even when the ape stands erect. The others have arms that are relatively longer than a man's, it is true, which indicates a more prolonged existence as branch swingers, but they, gorilla, chimpanzee and orangutan alike have been clearly handicapped by their size. The bigger you get the more cramping a tree becomes, and the great apes that share the present with us all have legs that are too short for fully effective walking. There have been far too many million years spent squatting in crotches of trees, with large bodies and long brachiating arms. However there is little doubt that the ancient gibbons from whom we may have leaped had much shorter arms than those now living, or that the great apes that were dominant among the trees of the Miocene forests had body and legs in more human proportion. In the end the difference seems to be how big and heavy were we when we abandoned our cradle on the tree top, and how much brain we had already acquired before we found ourselves back upon the ground.

The argument in favor of the earlier and lighter start rests upon the foot. In the three large apes the tarsal bones of the foot, those numerous small bones which lie behind the metatarsals and form the instep, have undergone a conspicuous shortening. The shortening appears to be the direct result of weight of a large animal on a foot which has already become completely adapted for arboreal life. In this kind of foot the body weight is thrown on to the front tarsal bones and in order to carry it better the bones have become compressed, in effect almost as though they have been crushed! The interesting point is that the gibbon foot does not show this and neither does ours; and the conclusion drawn is that our early ancestors must have abandoned the trees and taken up bipedal locomotion exclusively at a stage when they were no larger or heavier than the modern gibbon, and that they increased in bulk after they had assumed a truly erect posture, using the heel for support of the body weight and thus relieving the tarsal bones. It is certainly a far-reaching conclusion to put on to a few bones, yet nevertheless it may be true. And it suggests that the gorilla, for instance, which as an adult is almost as fully grounded as we are, has left its more elevated abode too late to make a satisfactory job of the necessary transformations.

A good argument demands two sides more or less equally supplied with ammunition, and the exercise of human wit in unimpassioned debate is as distinctively human as any quality man possesses. And those who think that we grew large and heavy before we came down to earth have at least as much to say as the gibbonites. There are in fact so many points of similarity between the structure of the great apes and man that there is altogether too much that may be said about it and too much that has already been said. One extreme is often as bad as another, and we have another case here of the middle of the road being a better path than the ditch on either side. If we had gone to ground in the late Oligocene before the gibbon and the giant apes-to-be had separated along their different paths I suspect we should have turned out to be quadrupeds, running on all fours at least in the manner of baboons. We would then have avoided some of the defeats we usually suffer in our everlasting fight against the force of gravity, although when all is said, I much prefer to be the most elegant of the apes than a dog-shaped monkey, no matter how intelligent, colorful and tailless it became. Yet the more I think about this the more I realise it is sheer prejudice. We are all so familiar with the way we look that it seems shocking, if not actually indecent, to imagine that we could appear altogether different and still retain feeling of being our inward human selves. Beauty lies only in the eyes of the beholder is a fitting phrase when humanity looks in the mirror. And in the literal sense of the words it seems to me we have shown astonishing arrogance in saying that man has been made in the image of God.

If we had waited however until we had reached a stage like the modern heavy apes before we started our career as two-footed travelers I doubt that we would have made much of a success of it. The odds against us would have been too great and it is no accident that more kinds of giant apes have fallen by the wayside than have lived to see the light of today. It is more likely that early in Miocene time, when the giant apes were not so large as they were going to be but were already more advanced than their gibbonish ancestors, that the apes with human destiny started on their great adventure. We were already becoming large and were beginning to suffer a little from claustrophobia, as the outer ends of branches began to break beneath our weight and we were restricted more and more to the larger boughs. Food and, above all, safety were still to be found in the trees, but the tree top pathways such as monkeys and gibbons use even now became impossible for the heavier-bodied apes. The chain broke at its weakest link, where tree and tree come together, and only a moderate increase in weight would have compelled the creatures to travel from tree to tree along the ground instead of from branch to branch. Body bulk put us intermittently upon the ground with life itself at stake for those who lingered there too long. The supporting heel and the sprinting foot were products of the mad dash from one tree base to another, with the devil or some other forerunner of a leopard ready to take the hindermost.

Yet running for your life, whatever the immediate cause, is more than a pair of spring-like feet with bones all aligned in the direction of travel. An ape scampers, a man does not. He runs with great extension of his legs, finishing each stride with a real drive; and in modern man the muscle which finishes swinging back the thigh in this final thrust is the powerful and massive buttock. All the swelling curves of thighs and calves that give such pleasure to the human eye are the products of a desperate existence, of a need to run like the wind at times or else fail to run at all. Buttocks and broad pelvic bones swung into serviceable position mark us off from other creatures as strikingly as any structural feature we possess. The way a man walks is the way only a man walks, and our ends have shaped our destiny in a most surprising manner.

No man can be ancestral to his grandfather. There are no exceptions and the simple-minded quality of this statement does not detract from its importance as a rule when arranging fossil remains in sequence. It also applies to such questions as whether a chimpanzee or a gorilla is ancestral to man, questions which are actually nonsense. At the best a living ape merely illustrates a stage that we might have passed through at some time or other, but not in any exact sense. And in the same way a fossil of a sub-human being of, say, a million or half a million years ago may appear to be extremely primitive and yet be contemporary with beings that rank as Homo if not Sapiens. It cannot be the ancestor, no matter how fitting its nature may be, but it may be more or less similar to what an ancestor may have been at an earlier time. This is what makes piecing the human story together from fossil fragments so difficult. Fossil remains are coming in faster than ever but the

time concerned is so vast and the story itself so much more
than the history of the particular type which has finally survived that at the most we have only a few odd pieces of the
puzzle, pieces which are out of order in time as well as space.
We need to make what we can of them, even though different
minds have filled in between in different ways. Yet clearly the
road we took departed from typical tropical forests and led
into more open lands. Somewhere along this route we found
our manhood.

A possible starting place, although I do not believe it is the
one we want, takes us back at least twenty-five million years
to the Lower Miocene in East Africa, where a series of lake
deposits near Victoria Nyanza in Kenya have yielded a remarkable collection of animal remains. Some are of mastodons and
rhinoceros. Some are of two-toed herbivores that have only
outlandish names of Latin or Greek derivation, many are rodents including an ancestral 'Spring Hare', but the most abundant large animals are apes. More than two hundred finds of
apes have been made in contrast to less than fifty from all other
sources. The fauna as a whole appears to have lived in a relatively open wooded country and cannot have belonged to a
true tropical forest. Some of the apes were as large as a gorilla,
others no bigger than a gibbon, although the commonest of
the larger kinds, which goes by the suggestive name Proconsul, was lightly built and slender bodied, with fore and hind
legs of nearly equal length, apparently running upon all fours.
It is of such a type that it might have been the ancestors of
the large brachiating apes that flourished somewhat later
among the denser forests of Southern Asia, except that having
left the trees for more or less open spaces why would they
have returned? Or the apes might equally well have led to the
human stocks, except that being already four-footed and upon
the ground, what could have brought them on to their hind
legs alone? It seems to me that we are afforded a glimpse of

a time and place where our fore-runners, using this word in its double sense, might have been present. Yet it is more likely I think that Proconsul has left no modern descendants, that it took to the ground prematurely and was finally engulfed by circumstances. The happy accident, from the point of view of fossil hunters, of having a ready-made, self-operating lakeside cemetery adds weight to the bones but not to their significance. Too much is missing however to be dogmatic.

Yet Africa has been surprisingly productive in the matter of bones in recent years, of a kind that seem neither ape nor human but something of both. Until these turned up, the earlier finds suggested that the main line of ape evolution led straight up to gorillas and chimpanzees, which was a view which made any understanding of human origins very difficult. Man as a highly special kind of ape in many ways became hard to explain and the discoveries of the last quarter century have brought relief and have changed the picture. The remains are as man-ape as any could be and are called the australopiths or southern apes. The oldest so far discovered come from the lower Pliocene, perhaps ten million years ago. The most recent belong to the middle Pleistocene and were certainly contemporaries of man. It is a tantalizing thought. The modern apes caricature us and have bothered us severely by their presence. Now it seems we parted company with their ancestors so long ago we can look on them dispassionately and perhaps even with compassion. But these other creatures! More and more it seems we started together along the human path, that the australopiths slowed up somewhere along the way, and until very recently were still alive. I would like to have met them, although the problem of co-existence on any sort of mutually tolerant basis would be far greater than that now troubling mankind. For these are not so much caricatures of the human race, they are to all intent what we used to be and may have been not so very long ago.

They are startling, to say the least. In fact when only teeth were known, teeth which came from Pleistocene beds in Java and China no more than a million years old, the teeth were recognized as being practically human. But they were immense and it looked for awhile that we might well have had giants ten feet high as ancestors. Yet the African finds show that while the teeth belonged to a large face, the face was out of all proportion to its owner. The outsize face and teeth belonged to creatures that were comparatively small and slender bodied, about the size of chimpanzees but much more lightly built and with considerably more brain. What we would have done with them had they survived I do not know. They would have been too intelligent to have been kept in captivity, too shocking to have lived with, and we would probably have identified them as the devil and exterminated them as quickly as possible. In fact we may have done so.

Most of the man-ape remains come from a series of caves in South Africa, all of Pleistocene age. Teeth of the same distinctive kind however are known from middle Pliocene beds in India, so that the man-apes appear to have roamed the earth in all likelihood for the last ten million years. It happens that those we know most about are the most recent. And this is what we know: they walked on two legs and they walked erect; the hole in the base of the skull through which the spinal cord passes and enlarges to form the brain is placed much farther forwards than it is in any ape, indicating a balancing of the head on top of the neck; an erect head means a neck held vertically; a vertical neck means a vertical back and an upright gait on the hind legs alone; and the extremely human pelvic bones are of a sort to which large leg-stretching buttocks are attached. The lightweight, large faced beings stood virtually as erect as we do. And if their first condition was in anyway like their last, they took to caves for shelter, roamed the wide earth and lived by their wits and a fast pair of heels.

Whether they threw stones we do not know.

So I believe men were bipeds first and foremost, with large faces and small brains; later they became bigger bipeds with small faces and large brains. If the trend continues, our present standards of physical beauty will have to change.

7

MATRIX OF THE MIND

Wᴴᴬᵀ is man? The question
is as simple and as difficult to answer as if I had asked 'who are
you?' Your name comes pat but it tells me little. Thereafter
the answer gets more and more involved. And we feel we should
be able to point somewhere along the line of man's emergence
and say here is where man first became man, that before this
he was not human but something else. Some of us say that
man has a soul and animals do not, which suggests to a biologist that we must have acquired it at a certain stage just as we
acquired a thumb or a heel, or perhaps a sense of humor, although the statement concerns an assumption, not an observation, and you cannot appraise the soul of a dead man or a
dead half-man by looking at his bones.

We know we are human, but that comes from self-knowl-
edge as much as from looking around us, and the more we
try to define what it means the more elusive it becomes. All
the little differences between a man and an ape add up to a
lot when put together but it is not easy to select any one feature as the distinctive criterion. A German zoologist of the
late nineteenth century, at a time when the argument was run-

ning strong, suggested that man is to be distinguished from the apes by his buttocks and his calves, implying erectness of stature and a striding walk. This measure definitely admits the australopiths to our assembly. It also suggests how hard it is to find a better measure. Perhaps the question itself is at fault, is too simply put, and no single answer can suffice. In any case I believe this is true, for it is the experience of scientists and philosophers alike, that a good question always raises another, often enough a host of them. And this is our present difficulty. We are so many things all at once. As individuals we are something that happens between the time of our conception and the day of our death. As a population we have trends and qualities that only populations can possess. And both as a kind of animal and as a population we have had a long transforming history. All of it is human, whether we share it with a shrew or an ape, or whether it is ours alone.

Having put ourselves upon our two hind feet we should I think take advantage of the elevation and look for a moment at the whole picture in its four dimensions. Time especially looms large and we need to get the feel of it.

Time is somewhat like space. We measure what is close to us in different units from what lies far away. We can speak of the twenty or twenty-five million years it may have taken the earliest qualifying mammal to perfect itself and climb into the trees as simply as a chunk of time too remote in every way to have much meaning. We can think of the next twenty-five million years, from the end of the Eocene to the end of the Miocene, as of greater import. We are closer to it for one thing, and during that period we at least became partly human. It is still an enormous stretch of time. We can discuss it and reconstruct from various clues the events which took place in it, but we cannot really sense the passing of so many years or lifetimes. Yet the end of the period brings us to within twelve million years of our present time. Eleven of these are of the Pliocene period and because the period is shorter and ends no more than one million years ago, the pace seems to quicken. During this period we take our first faltering steps as bipeds upon the ground and emerge as men of a kind which at least we cannot repudiate. The last million years, the Pleistocene, sees the beginning and what we hope is the end of the ice age. A million years is still a long time, but it is measured in thousands of years and we now begin to feel the enormity of the passing time. Out of the ice age, about ten thousand years ago, our modern world begins to take form, and with the last retreat of the ice we can almost see ourselves emerging from the mists of time plodding along the road to the present and the future and making records as we go.

At all stages we have gathered something that has become an essential part of our humanity. If we share much of it with apes or monkeys or the lesser hairy folk, we should cherish it the more, not less. If we find ourselves to be the descendants of the only one of a dozen subhuman types that have existed, we should appreciate our luck in being so exclusively the masters of this globe, if luck it is. We carry the torch for more than we know, perhaps for more than we can ever know. Of the host of ape-like beings that evolved among the trees of the Miocene forests only four have survived, four which have gone on changing in certain ways during subsequent time. Of many man-apes that evolved on the ground during the Pliocene period only a few were around when the ice age commenced. And of the few that started on the final lap just one has survived. Could it be that we are living out the rhyme of The Ten Little Indians, with only one to go?

Whatever the future may hold, I would like to know what has happened so far. Whether the human race is immortal or is about to die from atomic indigestion makes no difference. My own curiosity is all the greater for knowing that I have no more than a certain small number of years to live. In fact both my recognition of my mortality and my compelling urge to embrace eternity in my lifetime are qualities outstandingly and uniquely human. Above all, to put it bluntly, I want to know what made a monkey into a man, apart from the question of stature and the lack of a tail. Just what is our saving grace, if any?

We left our story at a critical place, with an apish creature running on two legs among open woodland, a creature with a long history behind it and a fantastic future before it. Already it is far along the way we have taken.

Think for a moment of some of the differences between an animal such as the shrew and any ape or monkey, other than those of skeleton and locomotion. The body of an ape is bigger, much bigger, and the vital ratio of heat produced to heat lost in a certain time is very much higher: energy is conserved and the food that must be consumed to keep the living flame burning is much less in proportion to the body's weight. For the advantages of growing larger are real and great and this is one of them. There are others. An owl may snatch a shrew and swallow it whole, but a contest between an owl and a monkey would leave the bird naked. Yet more important I think is the general prolongation of life itself, for as size increases the life span lengthens. No shrew sees the same season twice, but apes and the larger monkeys may live forty to fifty years before death from old age overtakes them. As the earth turns, experience grows and an ape gets wiser. Memory and intelligence are given time to ripen. The question is what kind of memory and what kind of intelligence?

I realise that neither as biologists nor as egocentric humans should we look upon a living ape as one of our forefathers, for both the time and the ape have changed since anything like that was one of ours. Yet if we are to see more than dry bones in a fossil ancestor we must at last look at a chimpanzee face to face. It is a somewhat unnerving experience, I admit, for under such circumstances a chimpanzee stares back with as much evidence of intelligent curiosity as we ourselves exhibit. Naturally it gets tired of the view soonest and is all too likely to close the interview on a somewhat vulgar note, a termination which itself drives home the possibly unwelcome fact of kinship. Chimpanzees are certainly not man-apes of the kind we were a dozen million years ago, but in spite of their shortened legs and overlong arms, in spite of their having become more set in their ways in consequence of that extra time amid tropical forests, they are in size of body and kind of brain more or less what we used to be. What a chimpanzee is and is not, what it does and what it cannot or will not do is of vital interest to inquiring man, for chimpanzee brain and chimpanzee mind show us in living form just how far the arboreal adventure alone has been able to take them, and by the same token how far it probably took our own.

The brain of modern man is amazingly large: three pounds of the stuff, more or less, in the average adult, with males supplied with a few extra ounces of doubtful significance. It is more customary to express the three pounds as 1400 cubic centimeters since this is the measure used for making comparisons, for often it is easier to estimate the space a brain occupies than it is to weigh the brain itself. Brain weight or brain volume, however, are only rough indications of intelligence. The brain of the brilliant, encyclopedic and bigoted anatomist Cuvier exceeded eighteen hundred cubic centimeters, nearly a pound heavier than the average. Yet Anatole France who was a wiser man with greater insight, although less stuffed with information, had a brain of only eleven hundred cubic centimeters capacity, more than half a pound below average! It is hard to say which of the two brains was the better, for they sustained minds of such different quality. Cuvier's clearly had the more capacious memory and there is no doubt that memory takes up room as definitely as any other filing cabinet.

We are born with a brain weighing about twelve ounces, occupying a little less than four hundred cubic centimeters. The quantity is an interesting one for it is also the size of the brain of microcephalic idiots, those unfortunates who remain literally pinheads. It is also approximately the amount of brain a chimpanzee possesses, although a chimpanzee is as far from being an idiot as a baby is, for the one is a finished product of a certain limited kind and the other an unfinished stage of a more elaborate production.

A brain and its sense organs must be taken together. Certainly this does not go without saying, for a mind and its senses are so interwoven we cannot imagine one without the other, whether they be human or chimpanzee. Describe the brain and you describe the being. The difficulty is to do so.

The early man apes of the Pliocene had brains of about the same size and shape as the chimpanzees have now, about four hundred cubic centimeters more or less, with the frontal region relatively low. We know little more than that about the fossils but the living ape has much to tell, if not to say. Apart from volume and the relative size of the frontal lobes the chimpanzee brain is very much like our own. Both the brain and its owner are disconcertingly human in too many ways, and while we intuitively know that the differences between us are tremendously significant they are not differences at all easily defined. If you think otherwise then I suggest you spend a profitable and chastening evening working them out, preferably as though for the enlightenment of an ignorant person from another planet.

When a dog encounters something strange it sniffs it all over. The most important and meaningful impressions are those of smell. A dog's memory, like that of most mammals, is richly stored with the scents of past experiences and the lessons associated with them. Compared with a wet-nosed dog or deer our organ for smell hardly exists. Our nose serves mainly for the passage of air to and from our lungs, and I find it next to impossible to imagine a mental world in which odors are more dominant than light and sound. Yet smell brains in which the greater part of the brain cortex is devoted to the analysis and recording of scents are common and primitive among mammalian creatures. The mind must live in an intimate world of airborne chemistry which may be wonderful for those that have it but seems limited to those without.

When a child or a chimpanzee or any uninhibited human encounters a strange object, sniffing is just about the last thing that is done, if at all. We react by picking it up, handling it in various ways and looking at it from all sides. We get the feel of hardness, texture and shape through our fingers, the pattern of color and light and shade through the retina of our eyes, and impressions of solidity and contours through the action of focussing and operational eye muscles. As a rule you don't just see form, your eyes unconsciously trace the outline with imperceptible movements, the truth of which you can test on the next fascinating curve you come across. Our minds are dominated by sight instead of smell, speaking both for myself and the chimpanzee, and our brain shows it. The visual cortex in the brain of each of us is very large but the smell cortex is so small, actually and relatively, that it hardly ranks at all. A chimpanzee has eyes as good as if not better than mine, for sensing color, recording detail, and for analysis in the three dimensions of space; and it has as much of its brain set aside for the projection of these activities as I have. Thus far at least we are alike, and it means I think that the sight brain had fully replaced the smell brain by the time we left the forest for more open spaces. Smell has become the cinderella of the senses and light now floods the mind to an extent that only birds know better.

When you and a chimpanzee start to examine each other,

each pair of eyes moves in unison. It is unnatural, unwise and usually impossible to move them independently. All movements have much the same end in view: to keep the image in focus and in the same register; and to serve this end the two sets of muscles attached to the eyeballs are in constant action. We move our eyes like a couple of searchlights always converging on the same single object no matter how much it moves to and fro or from side to side; and when the object is large, whether it be an apple close up or a distant mountain, the spotlight moves along its margins. Sight for us is vision in action, and memory of things seen is memory of visual images and of our own optic muscle movements. Close your eyes for a moment and picture a triangle: you can sense your eyes moving from point to point. And to all of this we add all the sensory impressions gathered from the skin and muscles of fingers and palms. The brain is enlarged between the regions set apart for vision and touch so that records of their past associations can be neatly stored. We have in fact a type of brain as highly distinctive as it can be, in which seeing and doing are in some ways indissoluble, but in this sense it is as typical of an ape, or even a monkey, as it is of a man. The roving eyes and the exploring fingers are at the root of that idle curiosity which characterizes all of us and unites us in a community of mischief ranging from throwing nuts to throwing atom bombs.

There is more to a brain than this however. There are centers governing the vital body functions; seats of emotion; other senses such as pain, taste and hearing. All constitute a single whole together with sight and touch and muscle sense. Yet the distinction remains. We and our fellow anthropoids are unique in the way we look out on the world around us, seeing in three dimensions and actually partaking of them with every glance we make. We are creatures so wedded to light and space that the human members of the group show no evidence of knowing where to stop. The urge to journey into outer space and see the back of the moon could only flourish in a mind of this sort, in a mind released from the old chemical servitude and hypnotised by the light of a star. The present impulse may be new in form but it stems from an old inheritance. We may have been grounded apes when we deserted the denser forests but we not only stood more or less erect, we gazed far and wide and appraised the distance and shape of what we saw. That was twelve million years ago when we had less than our present height and had little more brain than the chimpanzee.

What has happened since, in the long interval between this early Pliocene beginning and contemporary man with his over-sized head? The smallest human brain of those now living is that of the female Australian aborigine, which has a volume of about 850 cubic centimeters. This is only half the volume of the largest male Caucasian brains but its owner is fully human even if no genius. Living apes have brain volumes varying from 325 to 650 cubic centimeters. The fossil man-apes of Africa had brains ranging from 450 to 850 cubic centimeters. They bridge the gap so far as size alone is concerned, and the more obviously if we disregard the last million or half million years, for fossil human skulls no older than this suggest that the average brain volume was then no more than 800 to 1000 cubic centimeters. The final adjustment that brought the average brain volume up to its present value seems to have been fairly recent and rapid, speaking in terms of the whole event. In a general way we can say that the brain volume doubled during the ten million years or so of man-ape evolution in the Pliocene period, and that it has on the average doubled again during the last million years. No doubt the trend has been fairly steady but there is also little doubt that towards the end there has been an acceleration. Whether it still continues we would dearly like to know, although wishful thinking will not make it so.

It is unfortunate for our inquiry that the man-apes have all died out. We know the size and shape of their skulls, and something about their teeth; we know that they stood erect and had a general physique like that of a Bushman woman, that is of the smallest living human; and as far as we can tell they did not shape stones for use as tools or weapons, although the last of them were contemporaries both in time and place with primitive men who did. It is little enough but it tells us more than you might think, particularly when we consider how and where they lived, at least in the case of those that have been found.

The African remains, which are far more complete and numerous than any from other regions, come from caves scattered along a four-hundred mile escarpment in South Africa. None of these appears to be older than early Pleistocene, not more than a million years and possibly considerably less. They lived on beyond their kind in the unchanged African environment just as the four living apes have persisted in the continuing belt of tropical forest. And with them survived strange animals like primitive hyenas. The caves from which the skulls have come lie outside the tropics and there is no doubt that the man-apes were adapted to life in open country with scattered trees. They may have lived on a diet like that of the baboons with which they competed for caves, living on fruit, roots, insects, birds and their eggs, and virtually anything eatable; or they may have been hunters to some extent, although the absence of recognisable weapons makes this unlikely. Their teeth resemble ours much more closely than they do the apes.

The picture we get is peculiar, neither this nor that. The smallish body stands upright and runs like a man, and takes shelter in caves. The head has a large ape-like face with decidedly human teeth. The brain case is smaller than a man's but is larger than an ape's though much the same in shape. If our ancestors were such as these, we became men in bits and pieces. Human stature preceded human brains. Human teeth preceded the human face. And judging from the shape of these ancient African skulls, the back half of the human brain reached its peak before the fore part, which tells a story.

A brain, even such a small and seemingly simple one as that of a bee, is infinitely complex in its intimate structure and is amazing in its performance. When, as in this case, so much can be accomplished by so little, I am astonished that the great mammalian brains do no more than they do, with all respect to our own superior achievements. It suggests, to my mind at least, that we fail to put them to their full use, that both our present brain and its possible future developments contain potentialities as yet hardly dreamt of.

If you could lift away the side of the human skull you would see one half of the convoluted brain lying on a base line drawn roughly from the eye through the ear to the back of the skull. A deep groove runs down the middle, dividing the side you see into a fore part and a back part of more or less equal size. The back part contains the regions associated with vision, hearing and touch, with large areas lying between these in which the memories and associations connected with these senses are stored. Vision is at the back; the sense of touch lies just behind the central groove and along its whole length; the control area for all the body movements lies in the belt immediately on the groove's forward edge. And in front of all of this are the great lobes that extend into the forehead, the true ivory tower where that part of the brain is housed which is not concerned directly with either sensation or memory but seems to initiate and conduct the long range planning expeditions of the human mind. Occasionally someone suggests that since large parts of the forebrain elicit no direct response when electrically stimulated, and since so often when a part of the brain is damaged some other region seems to take over and compensate for the injury, that we may have a considerable excess of brain which we might well employ to greater profit. This I do not believe is true in the sense indicated. There is excess inasmuch as a great deal of duplication exists between the left and right sides, although it is far from being complete, and it is astonishing sometimes to what extent one side can serve for both. But this is a consequence of our essential symmetry and while it gives us a certain margin of cerebral safety it does not leave us with large unexploited areas of unknown capacity. In a general way we can say with some truth that the part of the brain lying behind the central groove is concerned with the present and the past, the part in front with the immediate and the more distant future, although all the evidence indicates that a brain or mind acts as a whole and not as separate departments.

When we compare this brain section by section with that of a chimpanzee we find two differences, one great and the other not so obvious: the association and memory areas lying between the primary sensory regions are less extensive in the chimpanzee, while the prefrontal regions so distinctive of the human brain are hardly represented at all. If brain structure has the significance I have assumed, then the chimpanzee brain is not so deeply involved in the past as ours and is hardly concerned with the future at all. This is the opinion of those who know chimpanzees best—that the chief difference between the great apes and human beings lies in the limitation of time in which the animal lives, that is, the extent to which it remembers back and considers forward. And yet within the limits of such time as their minds encompass a chimpanzee or an orang-utan behaves with true insight or intelligence when faced with new and man-made problems. Their brains are not essentially different from ours. They are just not so good.

Now the great difference in size between ape and human brain lies with the association areas and not with the primary regions. We neither see nor hear better than an ape or perhaps even as well, but the outlying areas of general and special sensibility are enormously increased. Our present concern is with the manner in which these increases have occurred, and the compelling reasons behind them, which is where the South African skulls are illuminating.

The brains contained by the man-ape skulls were about twice as large as those of apes of similar body size. The increase however was almost entirely in the regions lying behind the central groove, in the memory and association areas lying between the primary regions of sight, hearing and touch. There was very little increase in the frontal regions and the large-faced little people had large backs to their heads but more or less flat fronts, with foreheads in fact not so much receding as hardly there at all. Neither ape nor man, they stored experience of past events, of scenes and images, and of the feel of things handled, to a far greater extent and for longer time than their arboreal predecessors had been able to do. Past time became woven into the matrix of the mind more thoroughly than this planet had known before. But why? Neither the erect bipedal locomotion with its new fangled foot and bulging calf and buttock, with its balanced head and slender neck, nor the bulky expansion of the hinder half of the brain were acquired overnight. Taken together, for they may well have come together, the changes were of a magnitude that needed untold generations to evolve, for judging by all else we know the change from one generation to the next would have been imperceptible to our eyes. Horses are a case in point: from the Eocene to the present, horses in general have grown from dog-size to horse-size, but so many generations have passed in the process that the increase in size per generation is not measurable. In the Pliocene times we are here concerned with, horses as a group were still running on three-toed feet. There was a continuing pressure for horses to become larger without becoming slower, and much of horse evolution has concerned the maintenance of initial speed in spite of great increase in size.

Both spell safety of a sort. And what holds in principle for horses holds for grounded apes.

You can judge a man by the company he keeps is an old saying and a doubtful practice. Yet there is some truth in it and it should apply to man-apes as well as to our more snobbish kind. And man-apes possibly from the beginning of their grounded life have kept company with baboons. It is a curious assortment and some of our more disagreeable manners may have come from bad association instead of low caste inheritance. At least there is food for thought here and I feel we should give it some consideration.

Baboons are not nice, not even those with red and blue faces and red behinds. They are not even apes, in spite of the fact that the tails of some are so short as to be barely present. Baboons are monkeys that look like dogs. They bark, run on all fours, have a long snout and fang-like canines. But they are more intelligent than any dog or any other monkey, ranking only less than apes and men. They band together in troops, roam far and wide, and have evolved a form of social life that in some ways is just plain nasty. Being grounded monkeys rather than grounded apes they show us what we might have been had we also abandoned arboreal life before we were ready to walk effectively on our two hind feet. We would have avoided getting aching backs and numerous other ailments of a chronic kind but I doubt if we could ever have appreciated the beauty of a scene with a snout always in the centre of the stage.

Man-apes and baboons in Africa lived in the same territory, competed for the same caves for shelter, and for a long time ate the same kind of food; only as man-apes became hunters and more man-like could they have extended their diet to include the flesh of larger animals, perhaps including the baboon itself. For most of the long Pliocene time they lived in much the same environment and had to contend with the same general set of circumstances; and since man-apes as such are no longer with us but baboons abound, we can get some idea of how the man-apes may have lived by looking at their one-time companions.

As a rule when an animal senses danger it turns and runs and keeps on running, or it climbs a tree or dives for a burrow, or less often stands and fights. Baboons do none of these. They make for the nearest high rocks, as though garrisoning a citadel, and turn to watch. As a group they seem to know that unity is strength, and as individuals that there is wisdom in making a full appraisal of a situation that has disturbed them. They watch and listen with an intelligent curiosity and match the present situation with past experience. Memory serves a vital need and the more particularly because it is memory serving as the basis for action, for planned movement.

This is significant, for a planned action of even a simple kind calls for a certain form of imagination. You cannot decide on any course of action without to some degree picturing yourself doing it, and it is this that the frontal region of the brain appears to be concerned with. It is this part of the brain that is essential to self consciousness, the part that feels the limbs run or leap, that feels the movements of the hands and eyes, and knows the touch of the body. Baboon, ape and man-ape have or had it to a marked extent; we have developed it to an extraordinary extent. It is that part which enables an animal to know what it is doing, to remember what it has done, and to estimate what it might do. The life of a baboon and the somewhat similar life the man-apes lived is the kind that puts a survival premium on this quality of mind. The baboon has become the most intelligent of the monkeys. The man-apes in their time were the most intelligent of the apes, which we as their most likely descendants should be all too willing to admit.

8

EXPLODING BRAINS

$\mathcal{T}$HE pace changes. The ten million years of the Pliocene saw the rise of the man-apes as flat browed, erect pedestrians, better able to look backwards into memory than to think ahead. During the following half million or so years that elapsed between the latter part of the Pliocene and the middle of the Pleistocene, modern man came into being. The brain expanded, particularly toward the front, with almost explosive force compared with the slow changes of older ages. And since the end of this period, a few hundred thousand years ago, our brains have not improved in any apparent way. We acquired our distinctive humanity during an extremely short phase of our total history and one of our greatest needs is to understand both the nature of the change and the cause of it—for all present signs suggest that while the process may have since become suspended it is clearly and unhappily far from having reached a satisfactory conclusion.

The way of life of baboons and the way of life of man-apes in so far as it was like the life of baboons hardly accounts for what has happened, although in the last few years some biologists have seriously suggested that it does. To some extent it is one man's view against another, which after all is what minds are for. There is a healthy diversity of opinion which itself suggests we are inquiring into a very complex situation and it may well be that even opposing theories may each contain a part of the truth omitted by the other. The nature of family life enters strongly into all of them, using the term in a very broad-minded sense.

Few recreations are more absorbing than an hour or two spent at a zoo watching a colony of baboons. You do not need to be a biologist to appreciate what you see, for there is all the fascination of watching your neighbor's private life through a hole in the wall. The baboons look human enough to sustain the illusion and what they do seems to reflect our own activities in a decidedly flagrant form. The whole colony is the family, with harem groups centered about each fierce and dominant old male; with each individual knowing his place within the spatially fluctuating situation with an intense awareness. The old males guard their women; young females in heat try to attract them; bachelors sit and watch and keep their distance; mothers tend their babies. Fighting, mating, playing, grooming, nursing go on all the time. It goes hard with the socially unadjusted, and a young bachelor male must watch his step at every turn.

The question is did the human type of individual and the typical human family evolve from this sort of social grouping? It is possible, although I don't believe they did. If there is anything here however it concerns the circumstances of the subordinate male. Very briefly the argument runs like this: that in large family parties like those of baboons and, on a smaller scale, of the great apes, certain males become dominant by virtue of greater strength or fighting ability, or a more aggressive personality, and of the greater experience that comes with age. Younger or weaker or less aggressive males are kept at a distance. Primarily this refers to breeding. A few of the males sequester most of the females and sire almost all the offspring. Their own particular characteristics are passed on to the next generation rather than those of males who for one reason or another are unable to mate with the females. Yet the bachelor males are as potentially a threat to a dominant male as he is to them, except that they walk circumspectly and live more on the principle that he who mates and runs away lives to mate again. We have a situation in which danger in the form of powerful and vengeful males is continually present, a danger which influences all movements of the subordinates within the colony, whether related to breeding, feeding, fighting or anything else. The subordinate males must know exactly where they stand at all times, in the most literal meaning of the phrase, no matter how the group may shift within itself or from place to place. Spatial consciousness in continually changing surroundings, both of the individual's own position and of that of others is the ever present requirement, with the breeding premium serving as the prize for the highest awareness. This is but one side of it. On the other are the positive bonds holding mother and young together, and the relations between a dominant male and his harem. The unique quality in both ape and monkey societies appears to be this persistent interaction between the positive elements pulling together males and females, and mothers and young, and the negative forces of male antagonism. Out of it all, it is suggested, the better human brain has evolved in the course of continual selection of the more spatially conscious, and the better planners of action, as the fathers of the race. It might have happened this way, but obviously it hasn't made men out of monkeys in the case of baboons and I doubt whether the same circumstances could have made a man out of an ape. We may have started in this groove but we didn't stay in it.

How did the man-apes make their living and what kind of social and family organizations did they have? These are difficult questions to answer when all you have are a few bones found in a certain place together with some other remains, yet somewhere in their general situation lie our beginnings as distinctively peculiar human beings.

Under the conditions of life in fairly open country, such as baboons and macaque monkeys at present enjoy, a certain amount of banding together for mutual protection seems to be essential, and under similar conditions there is little doubt that the man-apes would have done the same. Nor is there much doubt that the original type of family group at the beginning of the man-ape phase was more like that of existing great apes than the monogamous kind we now have, and were groups consisting of a dominant male, one or several less dominant males, a larger number of females, together with young. Such a unit could forage as a selfcontained group as long as the food consisted of the general mixed kind typical of apes and baboons to this day. The important question is when did more or less indiscriminate scrounging become augmented or replaced by the hunting of larger animals? This was the crucial turning point.

No shaped stones or other recognisable tools have been found near the remains of the man-apes, either in the caves or outside them, although the greatest living experts have searched for them. The only safe conclusion is that they were not made, at least not in any form that can be recognised as having been fashioned by hands to any extent at all. The further conclusion that weapons and tools were not employed at all goes too far and is I think entirely unjustified. Monkeys and apes have an unpleasant tendency to throw things at passers-by below and apes at least are inclined to use sticks to reach edible objects otherwise out of reach. Man-apes, with their better brains, would have had a greater tendency, not less. And certainly, in my opinion without any doubt at all, stones and sticks were used as weapons and tools long before any attempts were made to fashion them. We were tool users long before we were tool makers.

The caves in which the man-ape remains have been found also contain the bones of baboons of a larger size than those now living, together with the bones of other large animals, bones which have been broken in a manner that would have made it possible to extract the marrow. The association is puzzling. One view is that since baboons rarely die in the caves inhabited by their colony but like most sick animals go off somewhere by themselves, a dying man-ape would have done the same and those that left their bones and skulls in the caves did not die natural deaths. There has been a cannibalistic streak running through both ancient and not-so-ancient man and it is possible that man-ape groups preyed upon one another as well as upon any other form of meat. Another viewpoint is that inasmuch as the man-apes did not fashion weapons and apparently made no use of fire, dark caves in which savage carnivores probably made their lairs would have been the last places in which they could have found security, and that the diverse bones, including those of the man-apes, are all the remains of the meals of tiger-like creatures who preyed upon all and sundry. Yet it seems to me that if modern baboons can make use of caves in leopard-infested country, without using weapons or needing to light up the darkness, the man-apes could have done so too. Perhaps they did and the great cats also got into the caves and occasionally slaughtered a lot of them for the benefit of fossil hunters of a later time. They may have used the caves in spite of this particular danger. They gained security of a kind but also a fear of the dark that has never left us.

Altogether I think it is reasonable to regard the more advanced man-apes as hunters who probably cooperated in groups and threw stones or otherwise employed them to kill animals which they took to the caves to feast upon and suck the bones. Without any natural weapons such as fangs or claws only a form of beachcombing would have been possible, but cooperative action in stoning a cornered animal and group activity in digging up roots with broken sticks set the course we have been following ever since. Now we use a gun and a fork. They are not so different.

I am no hunter. Yet I cannot imagine a more ridiculous situation than first of all establishing myself as a dominant male with even a small harem coveted by other men and then going off in a spirit of comradeship on a hunt for large game. The two are about as incompatible as they can possibly be. You cannot concentrate upon the hunt and watch your wives and some sneaking males at the same time. Under such circumstances meat-eaters have to choose between a full stomach and a full house and there is little doubt that once the hunting era of mankind commenced, no matter how apish the hunters were, the system of over-aggressive and dominant males became a liability and the small human family with its monogamous bond took its place. For this was the only kind that could survive both as a breeding unit and as a hunting group either adequate by itself or capable of cooperating with other groups. Adult males undoubtedly must have worked together in the hunt for food and for protection of the group, at least to some extent, as they do in the case of both howling monkeys and wolves, and this by itself would have weeded out the most selfishly aggressive and uncooperative, paving the way or reinforcing the trend toward monogamous mating.

It is an old problem of nature that crops up all the time: how to integrate the egocentric male into society to the benefit of all concerned. In this case the old fashioned male dominated by his own chemistry, the slave of lust and anger, is less successful in propagating a race capable of survival than a male content with one female and able to control his emotions for cooperation in the hunt or in defense. In this sense we are more akin to the wolf than the baboon, for a wolf family is like the human and the male is intelligent, cooperative and solicitous. All of these qualities are selected in the course of time as leading to increased chances of survival and reproduction when pack hunting is the means of obtaining food. The most intelligent and the most cooperative are the most likely to survive and be in a position to continue the breed, and their offspring are more likely to be like themselves than like those that failed to reach maturity. So it was that the brain expanded forwards under pressure, generation by generation, and that it did so rapidly suggests that the pressures were extreme; and if we are to have any hope of continuing the process from where it has left us, the nature of these pressures and the manner in which the brain and the whole being responded to them are of vital interest.

Man in the tropics tends to vegetate if there are not too many of him and as long as he can safely pick fruit and dig tubers for his daily sustenance—tropical life did not give the final and violent shove that forced a man-ape into the mold of a man. Given any degree of comfort, we still relax into lethargy, into that kind of existence said to be enjoyed by a jellyfish floating in a tepid, tideless, twilight sea.

Our ancestors lusted after bigger and better game because there was too little of the sort of things they had previously been accustomed to eat. Either the tropical and semi-tropical belt became too greatly restricted or man-apes became more adventurous as their legs grew stronger and their running speed faster, or as the evidence seems to indicate it was something of both. Those that became men were able to respond to a challenge, those that did not were those that could not and they eventually dwindled and died. The challenge came from the earth itself, as it always does, for we—men, apes, horses and insects alike—are its children, not its creator. The earth's climate is forever changing, not only in seasonal sequences but on a cosmic scale both in time and severity, and as the wind blows so the tree bends.

During most of the mammalian time, from its beginning some seventy million years ago until late Miocene or early Pliocene, the world climate was warm from pole to ploe. The early horses, rhinoceroses, tapirs, mastodonts and a host of other large browsing animals lived in northern latitudes on a rather luxuriant vegetation typical of moist subtropical or temperate forests, late in the Miocene period at a time when the great apes were most abundant and successful. The climates of the earth were still fairly warm as recently as the beginning of the Pliocene period, for at that time alligators lived in the northern Great Plains of North America. Near the end of the period however there is evidence of definite climatic cooling in the northern hemisphere, intimations of the first great glacial advance of the Pleistocene, that chilly period which lingers with us yet.

Long before the ice caps started to form and reach toward the equator climatic zoning became extreme. The tropics narrowed. Temperate regions became extensive and sharply defined. Northern regions became more or less uninhabitable. The temperatures prevailing on the high plains of Asia and America became increasingly severe and fast-running, grass-cropping horses, deer and antelope took the place of the earlier foliage-browsing forms. Except for the narrowed tropical belt and its marginal territories which persisted as an asylum for those that couldn't change to meet the new conditions, most of the earth became an arena for those of fleeter foot or great adaptability. Instead of subsisting on the rich platter of lizards, insects, eggs, tropical fruit, and juicy roots the choice was restricted to flesh or grass. If you couldn't adjust to these then you either retreated towards the equator with the tropi-

cal vegetation or you failed to produce or raise your young
in sufficient numbers and so took the path to extinction. Our
ancestors were among those that rose to the challenge and
such were the circumstances that made our foreheads begin
to bulge. We can understand better how the pressures operated
however if we look closer at the effects they produced, and
perhaps tell whether or not the same or similar compulsions
are still in operation. Our human need is to become more
human than we are, if only we can find the key.

A man as a solitary individual has no meaning, except in the
case of temporary withdrawal. He is the product of his family
and takes his meaning from it. The family is man, whether we
project it to larger groups or not, and it is within the family
we should seek the essence of humanity. It goes a long way
back and it concerns both brains and infancy.

Our brains, apart from sheer size, differ from those of apes
and other folk in what lies well to the front of the central
groove, and in front of the broad belt of cortex associated with
the control, sense and memory of muscular actions. Most of
this distinctive region that sets us apart appears to be connected with the planning of future performance and with
conceptual thought, although I do not mean that this is
where the planner or thinker sits; many of us in fact spend
hardly any time there at all. Yet certain small areas concerned
with muscle control lie farther forward than the rest: those
that control the locked movements of the pair of eyes and, on
one side particularly, those concerned with the articulation of
speech. As human beings we are forever using our eyes as
instruments for the measuring of shapes and movements, recording them unconsciously at the time and in memory as
infinitesimal actions of our own; and we communicate with
one another by means of speech, employing a combination of
voice sound and facial gesture to serve as symbols of what is
within the mind. Between the two the brain and the mind have

grown. We are what we are to a great extent because our visual apparatus is of a certain kind and our brain reflects its nature; and because we have learned to talk and convey and think in terms of symbolic images. The eye brain goes back to the ape, but true speech is new and more than anything else, perhaps, has made us human. How did we acquire it?

Anyone who has time and tendency for contemplation is inclined now and then to take himself apart to see what makes him tick. It can be an enlightening experience to realise how various capacities and limitations work to produce the whole, and in the present connection I have found it fascinating to try to see what makes me speak.

I used to think that speech was mainly a matter of using my voice, but this simply isn't true. A baby squalls and so does a howling monkey, but this is only a signal that the baby or the monkey exists and is in a certain place. As far as I can see the signal has only three or four possible meanings: go away, stay near me or help me, or why was I born? The voice is a very old heirloom and has been widely employed throughout much of living time as a means of simple signalling over distances. We use it more for projecting speech across space but hardly need it for speech itself. You use no voice when you whisper supplications. Lips and tongue and a little breath are all-sufficient. A deaf person may lip read and hear nothing at all except in memory. Bellowing is old but the shape of a word is new, and that small region of the brain that frames articulation is also new; the intimate communication of human speech comes from the muzzle and not from the throat; to be tight-lipped or tongue-tied means not to speak, and even a ventrilo-quist has trouble in hiding the action. We first sang from the treetops or bayed to the moon, later learnt to whisper sweet nothings and then put the two together in a passionate serenade. I have no doubt that as lips and tongue and facial muscles conveyed more and more in face-to-face communications the voice was simultaneously employed. Speech grew as a whole, but the newer components conveyed the greater part of it, for speech is something to watch as well as hear and has been from the beginning. The brain shows it.

The beginnings of true speech cannot be divorced from the situation which evoked it. Both the internal and external requirements were complex, but if I had to select the outstanding feature of each I would say it was a loose tongue within and a lot of grass without. And the grass comes first!

Grass is so much everywhere that we take for granted it always has been like this, which is not true. Grasses came into being like everything else, during a certain time and in certain regions, about midway through the age of mammals and as a green cover for the uplands and savannas. Grasslands open to the sun and the wind offered opportunity to those that could take it, and during the Pliocene they grew vastly in extent as the climate became cooler and drier. Yet it is not so simple to eat grass as you might think. The soft succulent leaves of shrubs and trees that the forest animals ate were gentle on their teeth, but grass is rich in abrasive silicates and new types of grazing mammals evolved with harder and more complex teeth for cropping it. For such as these the grasslands offered abundant food, but with no forest cover to hide in their only escape from the pursuit of the great cats and dire-wolves was speed. Antelopes and horses and other two- and one-toed grass eaters arose that could run like the wind when danger approached. These became the most abundant kind of game and this abundance was undoubtedly the bait that drew incipient humans into the open, to fight for life in chilling winds and scorching sun but with wide horizons and the stars above.

Who did the hunting? Only those who were fast on their feet, nimble with their hands, quick to see and hear, and above all able to cooperate wholeheartedly with one another in the chase or trapping and capture of an animal. These lived, with all the more energy perhaps to repeat the performance. The dull of wit and uncooperative went hungry and left fewer progeny than the others to carry on the race. It was more important to obtain meat on the hoof than to take advantage of male lust or female heat or to indulge in vengeful anger on all other males. Groups that retained the old harem system either quickly died out or kept on as long as they could scrounging for food in the old fashioned way, each member on his or her own except when an indulgent overlord gave a tidbit to his favorite female of the moment. The future faded for those in whom the sex hormones continued to govern but opened for those whose brains assumed an over-riding control of emotional reactions. Flexibility of response replaced the old rigidity of action and male and female became one to one as living units. No other grouping can be seen to work under the new conditions: only complete cooperation between a man and a woman and their children serves to keep them alive, with all who can cooperating in obtaining meat and with the father cooperating with the mother in raising and training their offspring.

The human family, like that of the wolf, is in origin a hunting family, with monogamous mating, and intelligence and solicitude in training the young to hunt with the parents. Cooperative within the family, these early humans could have cooperated as hunting packs of larger and more effective size, as wolves do too, for cooperation once established tends to spread; but always at the base of it lies the intimate and intelligent interplay within the family, between male and female, mother and infant, father and young. Here is the home of man and the cradle of speech.

Cooperation to be effective demands communication, whether it be a signal from a pair of eyes, a growled alert, or whatever goes on in the silent enclave of a group of lions, or the sudden pointing of a human hand with an accompanying expression of face and voice. The early humans, armed only with wits and hands and what they could make of them, had to communicate or die. Communications of intent and strategy of forthcoming action made the difference between success and failure, between eating or not eating, between being eaten and not being eaten, between living and not living. Communication of patterns of thought, of symbols for objects and actions, was vital in the training of offspring to act like their parents and to continue the patterns in their turn. Speech in fact grew where it grows today, in the close bondage of infants and children with both male and female parents. The facial expressions and vocal noises unconsciously made with every action and emotion took on definite and meaningful association in the intimacy of family gatherings where faces are close and can be read. Without the family I believe there would have been no speech, and without grass I doubt if the family as we know it would have come into being. Without grass and the game it has supported we would have had little need for elaborate communication and our jaws would not have had to widen and our chins to grow out to make room inside for our tongues to wag in. And as the tongues wagged, so the brain grew.

9

THE ESSENCE

AS human beings we talk incessantly and think strange thoughts, yet this is only part of being human. Another quality emerges from the human family, although its roots go farther back than that, which is to many our greatest glory and our greatest hope: that which Wordsworth recognized when he wrote that heaven lies about us in our infancy, for he was closer to the biological fact than he could have known. Somewhere in the past, and not too long ago, we underwent an evolutionary twist and slipped into a new dimension where time took on a different meaning. Human time is unique and somewhat paradoxical. For it is not how much we have that is so significant as when we have it. We are the Peter Pans of this planet and grow up reluctantly, with the thought of the mother-goddess in the back of our minds as long as we live. We come slowly into the world, rise slowly to our full stature and reach maturity later than any other creature. The implications, looking both backwards and forwards, are great.

It began in the tree tops like so much else, when maternal monkeys failed to hang on to plural offspring, or vice versa, and progeny became restricted to one at a time. When this happened the last could be first instead of an also-run with no place to suckle or clutch. So long as several eggs started on their internal career together there was a race to finish in time and the more vigorous survived and the slower did not. When single births replaced litters it no longer mattered how long it took to develop and get born, and the way was opened for the forcing of the most precious of human qualities.

Getting born is merely one hazard out of many, and you and I needed as much luck in getting started as in being launched alive. Apart from the to-be or not-to-be question of conception itself, when an egg and one of a million sperm get together in the upper reaches of the maternal tubes, the test that we all have had to pass with perfection was our implantation in the wall of the womb. Anything less and we would not be here, for imperfection spells failure either at once or sometime later in the form of an early abortion. In fact more human embryos fall by the way at a small and unnoticed stage than continue through to term. The danger is great and much of it due to gravity.

Gravity is no problem for four-footed beasts who run with their bodies horizontal to the ground. Their eggs have to be coaxed along the tubes by one means or another and when they arrive at the place where they are meant to be implanted they can afford to make an almost casual contact with the maternal tissue. They are rarely disturbed in the even tenure of their ways and can establish their connections without hazard and in the beginning with only minimal contact. When the same system is more or less upended as in a monkey the force of gravity aids in causing the cleaving egg to descend the tube and appears to be somewhat other than helpful when the wider passage of the implanting region is reached. If you are sliding precipitously down a cliff you dig your heels in as soon as you get a chance and hang on for your life—delay may well be fatal. A monkey egg implants with promptitude, anchoring the embryo-to-be quickly and firmly to the lining of the womb. What happens in apes with their more thorough-going uprightness I do not know, and while as an embryologist I would like to know, I cringe at the thought that an ape should be murdered to satisfy such curiosity, let alone at the slaughter that would be necessary to supply this single piece of information.

Even monkeys are all too human, especially for their own good, for they are afflicted by the same diseases as pester us. Whether our giving them poliomyelitis in an experimental effort to find a cure for the disease in ourselves can be justified by anything more than a heartless expediency, I have my doubts. Who gets sacrificed for the sake of whom is an ever present dilemma for a hungry, increasing, and disease-riddled mankind. Conscience lies heavy upon us when to be humane means being human, and it foreshadows worse to come.

Yet whether or not ape embryos implant like those of monkeys or go further with their precautions, somewhere along the line of our ascending stature the planting of the egg took on a deeper form. The human egg, already cleaving, not only adheres quickly to the wall of the womb but burrows below the surface into the maternal tissue as truly as any parasite. Once safely embedded, neither force of gravity nor any strain or stress can easily dislodge the babe-to-be until the embryo has grown so large as to bulge out into the womb cavity, when any fault in construction makes itself felt and an abortion occurs. As far as I know, nothing like this can be found anywhere else in the whole animal kingdom; in no other kind does the young embryo so savagely invade the tissues of the maternal organism or at so early a stage of development. It has had both a cause and a consequence.

When you consider how frequently miscarriages occur in humans during the first few weeks of pregnancy even as it is,

I would be surprised if many pregnancies would be successful if the older and common process of implanting still prevailed. We put a woman to bed if there is any indication that an embryo is in danger of losing its hold, and it seems to me that this is significant and that the peculiarly human reaction of the embryo at the beginning of its development has been brought about by the attainment of erect stature together with the intensification of action that went with the change from foraging to hunting. No selection is so effective as the sorting of seeds and no weeding out would have been faster than one which let the slow-implanting eggs pass on and retained only those that made a quick invading response. No halfway measure would do: eggs or embryos either held their place or they didn't, and only those that did had any chance of contributing their qualities to the next generation. And rapidly, in one generation after another, as the fleet form of the human body took its shape, development gained a more intimate maternal association than ever had been known before.

This is but one aspect of our individual becoming. There is another which may be its outcome or which may be a quality gained independently. We develop in the womb for approximately nine months before we are born. So do the young of the three great apes, although in the case of the more primitive gibbon the gestation is for seven months only. The time is fairly long, though not exceptionally so, and even among the apes the pace has slowed. And except in contemporary civilization the human mother suckles her offspring well into the second year, which seems to be the average period for the apes as well. The basic pattern is fairly old: a slow development, considering the size of the infant at the time of birth—for at the other extreme the blue whale produces a two-ton baby at the end of nine months; and a late weaning. A gibbon mother has been known to nurse her offspring for more than two years and among human savages nursing usually continues for two or three years. Both prenatal life and infancy are greatly prolonged compared with that of most other forms of mammalian life. Yet humanly we are distinct. In certain ways hard to define, the living human texture is more finely woven than is any other kind. Human substance grows more slowly and burns with a steadier flame, not just in the beginning but throughout life. And I suspect, but do not know, that the unique quality of our development and growth is intimately connected with the avid reactions of the implanting egg, that it all comes from the complex change in the protoplasmic chemistry of the egg.

We each of us live an individual life that is remarkable not only for its length but the manner in which it is lived. Some other creatures whose blood is as hot as ours, such as the elephant and the parrot, live almost as long as we do, but their youthful time is quickly over and they live out their succession of years as sexually mature adults. Long life in other animals than ourselves is mainly a matter surviving in a fully completed state, with wear and tear kept under as close control as possible. We are different. It is as if you took two ends of the single year of the shrew and stretched it out to seventy. Every phase of life is drawn out, so that we reach our physical maturity at an age when most creatures of our size are already dying, we remain sexually mature for nearly twice as long again and, even more remarkable, persist for several decades in a postmature state. To what extent we attain mental and emotional maturity is hard to say. Some never reach it at all and others attain the fixed stubbornness and latent ferocity of a male gorilla all too soon. The human secret, in part at least, is the combination of youth and experience, the capacity to live without growing old, though your hair fall out and you finally drop in your tracks. Within the limits of mortality we remain human to the extent that we drink at the fountain of youth. This is as much a biological fact as it is a conclusion drawn from insight.

Whether the sub-human families operated by themselves or collectively in larger groups as occasion demanded, each small family puts its occasional egg, so to speak, into a single basket. And it is a general rule of nature that the fewer the eggs the more they must be watched over. The choice lies between some kind of mass production without much overseeing and the perfect handwrought product to be guarded if necessary with your life. And the new way of life of the hunter made both the perfection and the protection of the progeny vital to racial survival. The long drawn-out childhood was no accidental acquisition but something demanded by the new conditions, and the sternness of the command that brought it forth I find difficult to imagine.

Subhuman wits and unfashioned weapons were weak equipment for contending with new and savage forms of carnivores whether in competition for food or not, for the flesheaters probably took a man as readily as a deer. Judging from the outcome those that survived were those who combined the wisdom of experience with the resiliency and adaptability of youth; and while firsthand experiences cut closer to the bone, those communicated by parents or other elders also carried survival value. The best parents saw more grandchildren than those who were less careful or less intelligent or less able to communicate or less cooperative. With starvation and danger ready to cut down on all but the first of these, the human family was trimmed to the shape we know. Childhood cannot be divorced from parenthood. The mother nurtures her young, protects them and trains them in the technique of family maintenance, tightening the emotional bonds between one generation and the next. The father communicates the skills of hunting, defense, and the finding of shelter. Intelligence, the ability to communicate, and the solicitude of parenthood all combined to sustain the life both of parents and young alike. Poor fathers were worse than useless and were genealogical dead ends. Mothers have been good mothers for time out of mind, certainly as long as the age of mammals itself, but fathers as such are new to this earth; for fatherhood and paternity are two very different things, as any court of law can testify, and the solicitous male is a new invention, with regard to his offspring at least. In man and wolf and beaver the male belatedly takes his full part in the scheme of things.

Relationships have more than one side. The inevitable selection of cooperative male and female parents, progressively inclined to raise and train strong and equally cooperative offspring, as the more successful propagators of the race, also called for a corresponding response in their progeny. Obviously it was at least as important to produce children capable of understanding the facial, manual and vocal gestures employed in conveying symbolic images of actions and things as it was to make them. And if wits were at such a premium clearly no set of rules could be relied upon implicitly for very long: intelligence exists primarily to cope with changing circumstances and to become set in your ways whether by instinct or by indoctrination is equivalent to abdication and opens the door to extinction. Only the young can readily learn or be taught easily, whether by experience or by parents and their kind, and in the past of which I speak, to learn longest meant to live longest. Here was the force that pulled youth through the years to a later and later maturity. Under the circumstances it led I think to communities consisting for the most part of young breeding individuals at the peak of their physical performance, still young enough to learn from new experience and to modify precept, yet old enough to transmit their own heritage. Individual human or subhuman life may not have been notably much longer than that of other large mammals.

The important difference I believe was the retention of the juvenile adaptability and capacity to learn for at least twenty to thirty years, long enough that is to leave competent successors before you came to an untimely end. Youthfulness was prolonged by necessity to an extent unheard of, compatible with successful propagation, and this I am convinced is the essence of our humanity. We have since become more adept at living out our whole potential time, so that the proportion of youth to age decreases and the populations age. Our danger now I think is that we ripen too richly in the time at our disposal and lose our essential freshness and the exhilarating employment of the mind for its joyful and perhaps desperate business. But the three score and ten years that we lay claim to I doubt were ever in the cards. We stretched our youth to meet requirements. That we live so long when we fail to die by accident or violence I believe is one of nature's unpremeditated consequences. Our problem now is to remain human in spite of growing older, to keep the keen edge of living and to fuse the intelligence and the heart of youth with the wisdom that comes with time. This is what Jesus had in mind when he said that unless you are like a little child you cannot enter the kingdom. Child-like, he said, not childish.

10

ICE, FIRE AND STONES

THE question when did man become man receives different answers according to the way we measure him. We call ourselves Homo sapiens, the wise man. Others, not so old but known only by their bones, are admitted as men but not as wise: so we call them Homo neanderthalensis or some other name containing Homo but not sapiens. When we look at more ancient remains with smaller skulls and larger eyebrow ridges we drop Homo and take refuge in outlandish names: Sinanthropus for Pekin man and Pithecanthropus for Java man; the best we can manage, without too obvious condescension, is to allow them 'anthropus,' a sort of back-door acknowledgement. The man-apes at first were not received at all: Australopithecus means southern ape, and even the types found in the different caves were given different names. Now there is an increasing tendency to call a spade a spade, and to call a man a man even if he stands with a stoop. The man-apes of South Africa become Homo transvaalensis, the men of the Transvaal—a status that reflects their stature. Java man and Pekin man become Homo erectus, upright but far from righteous. While Homo sapiens embraces not only modern man but the neanderthal and other types no longer living, whose skulls were thicker than ours but whose brains may have been no worse; and we can still retain the privilege of distinguishing between one wise man and another—but we recognize their humanity first and their differences later. It simplifies the picture and shows man advancing on a wider front through the last million years of earthly time. This is the period that concerns us most.

The last million years, except for the recent ten thousand years of post-glacial time, comprise the Pleistocene. The name is supposed to include both the beginning and the end of the ice age from which we were thought to have finally emerged, but the more we know about the ice age as a whole this becomes more of a hope than a promise. Within this period the ice has come and gone on a large scale not once but four times, with evidence of fluctuations of cold and lesser cold within each glacial surge, and of one chilly period that just failed to bring the ice. The climatic pendulum swung with violence compared with the slow changes in the ages that went before. Along this route, shaken into action by the earth itself, we get glimpses of early humans shivering or sweating as they struggled to cope with the elements and the beasts. The new and the old survived alongside one another and are not necessarily discovered in the order of their arrival, which tends to be confusing.

Somewhere we need to find a vantage point where we can look both forwards and backwards—there are too many valleys and crests to see across all at once. The sharpest picture I think is that of Pekin man with his brain at a halfway stage between man-ape and modern man, who lived when two ice caps had come and gone and two more were yet to come. By the time the Pekin folk were going about their business in China the polar ice had already gripped the northern lands for some sixty thousand years, had withdrawn for much the same length of time and had returned once more for an equally prolonged visitation. When the ice had melted for the second time but some of its chill was still in the air, the Pekinese haunted the caves of northern China and left us skulls to find. Before them stretched the long interglacial period that lasted about two hundred thousand years, only to be followed by two further glacial periods with a shorter interglacial period in between. The journey is long by any reckoning but at least it is possible from here to feel the burden of travel and to sense the distance ahead.

Pekin man ranks in many ways. He had a forehead, though not too like our own, and a brain that was small only in terms of the present average, one that ranged from about 900 cubic centimeters to 1250, well within the lower range of modern humans'. The Pekinese had clearly come a long way both as inventors and as collectors, although with their big confluent eyebrow ridges they were anything but pretty.

The Pekin caves however have yielded both too much and too little—too many skulls and not enough bones, at least not enough bones of the right kind. In fact the picture we get of the caves is more of a dining hall than a cemetery. Bones are there but they are the bones of ancient deer and other fast-running creatures, and there are patches of blackened earth which show that the cave inhabitants had fire. They also made and used stone tools of two very distinct kinds: small flaked scrapers and heavy choppers. Moreover the choppers, which were made to fit the palm of a hand, show that the Pekinese were right-handed, except perhaps for an occasional left-handed individual. The point is that they were lopsided in use of hand and brain, as choppers and skulls both testify. The skulls however are not only accompanied by the wrong kind of bones and hardly at all by any that are human but are remarkable inasmuch as they have been broken away at the base in a manner most unlikely to have been accidental. What can we make of it all?

They were firelighters, that much seems certain, for fires do not break out by themselves inside caves, but whether fire served to maintain warmth, to cook meat, or to scare away carnivorous intruders is hard to say—once fires were lit they would have served for all three and if at first one took preference and led the way to other uses, I think it would have been as a weapon to keep or drive the great cats out of the caves that they used as lairs. Saber-toothed tigers made poor companions inside a dark cave, although with such beasts excluded caves offered both shelter from the elements and from attack. But the discovery how to make and maintain a fire, possibly the greatest single discovery a mammal ever made, must have been learnt the hard way and for a good reason. A taste for burnt meat acquired in combing the woods after a forest fire seems to me to be an insufficient motive, and a morbid taste in any case to begin with. Yet the minds that saw the effect of fire, saw how to exploit fire to their own advantage, and found out how to make fire may have had the capacity to make an atom bomb under other cicumstances. Symbolic or abstract thought was required for both, and in the final phases a practical exploitation, although in comparing one mind with another we should remember that rarely have any two minds been the same. Fire must have passed through three phases: recognition of its power, the wish to use that power, and the action that made it possible. None of these is a mental quality to be taken for granted, and together they constitute a force that seems to be driving our present world to distraction if not destruction. The fire we lit a half million years ago is getting hotter.

Recognition and desire come first, exploitation later, and I imagine that maintenance of fire started by lightning long preceded the actual creation of fire by human hands unless fire itself was a by-product of another early human activity. This I think is entirely possible. Men have been striking sparks from the very beginning, ever since they began to bang one flint against another to flake off a cutting edge. Sitting on sun-scorched grass in dry heat the flint flakers must have all too often set fire to their surroundings and have had to move in a hurry. It is no idle metaphor that someone has to light a fire beneath us to get us going. This seems to me a much more likely manner of discovery and its further exploitation than snatching a burning brand from a burning forest. Primitive man like most of his modern representatives I am sure would have run from a forest fire as fast as any other scorched and startled creature. The thought of harnessing such an all-consuming monster would have been horrifying. In any event, and even though I have argued in a curve if not in a circle, I like the idea that man's discovery of the qualities, uses and means of making of fire happened on his own hearth, if one can employ this word a little prematurely. He felt the warmth, smelt his own scorching hair and hide, and knew the urge to get up and run. Fire in a sense was a gift from the gods, the gift of nature to the tool maker, and like most un-solicited gifts the final cost runs high.

Pekin man stayed warm and relatively safe within his caves except when hunting. Meat probably had become his principal food, for venison and vegetable as a rule are far apart and we know he ate the first of these. The question is where did he draw the line? Why are there so many skulls and hardly an-other human bone, and why are the skulls all broken open in the same peculiar manner? Did he hunt his own kind and eat them as readily as the next, and if so where are the rest of the bones? Perhaps he and his fellows were cannibals at the site of battle or ambush but took the heads home for a more leisurely, succulent and social feast. He may have paid his respects to his dead enemies or friends by sucking their brains and preserving their skulls, reckoning somehow that brain and the essential spirit were associated. If so, and it seems to me that something of this sort is implied, then we have here a specifically human habit depending on highly sophisticated thought. Cannibalism has been a common practice until recently, but except where it degenerated into a disgusting gluttony as it did with the Carib Indians discovered by Columbus, eating your dead enemy or drinking his blood from his empty skull has been a mark of greatest admiration and a wish to acquire his virtues. It was a spiritual acknowledgement from the first and in symbolic form survives even in Christian communion. It seems to me that Pekin man was strongly aware of mortality and of the spiritual quality of personality and was fully human.

He was a toolmaker, as his flakes and choppers demonstrate. And anyone who made both choppers and flakes had been making stone tools for an extraordinarily long time. Pekin man probably had been much as we know him for a good many years before he left his skulls in China caves for us to find; he could have been making his particular tools as early as the beginning of the first interglacial period, a hundred thousand years sooner than the time with which we associate him. Tools of his general sort belonging to those earlier days lie scattered across Asia and Africa. Yet I believe that the really striking feature about the tools is the right-handed fitting of the Pekin choppers. Right-handedness is a product of a left-sided brain and I cannot see that it is in any way an asset in itself. So often I would have been much better off if I had been ambidextrous and my left hand had been able to do what only my right hand can. High skill with one hand may have been all we were able to acquire, but two highly skilful hands would have been better than one. My left thumb is sore from being hit.

When that precision of skill evolved which gave mastery to the right eye and right hand in the vast majority of individuals and to the left eye and left hand in others, that is, to one side or the other, it was accompanied by a loosening of the tongue and a clearing of the throat. I am not sure whether we are dealing here with the unified wholeness of the human organism or whether our one-track minds have forced otherwise un-related actions into the same groove, but there is no doubt that one goes with another. When I start to draw, my right hand alone moves to hold the pencil, my eyes, particularly my right eye, follows the moving pencil point, my lips purse a little and tend to move accordingly, while my tongue at times seems to be doing its best to make the drawing itself. Fortunately I can keep my mouth closed and only I am conscious of the inner muscular mimicry, yet we have all seen it or experienced it. Somehow the wires are crossed between hands, eyes and tongues, and in such a way that one hand and one eye are strongly favored and at the same time tied to the tongue. The structure of the brain reflects this arrangement and on the left side, which controls more the right side of the body, there is a marked bulge somewhat above and behind the position of the left eye. It is not seen on the right side and it controls the articulatory movements of the tongue in speech. Control of the voice is another matter, but it is clear that sibilant and guttural speech and the dominant hand and eye movements are monitored through a single center on one side of the brain only. The fact that a left-handed child forced to change to right-handedness frequently becomes a bad stutterer shows how closely the tongue and one hand are strung together. I believe it implies that the complex system has evolved as a unit and not as a step by step feeding-in of new connections into a circuit already fully established, and that speech of the special quality that we now possess grew with the skills that finally made us so strongly one-sided, right or left as the case may be. Accordingly Pekin man with his right handed choppers and his lopsided brain wagged his tongue excessively and could speak in an elaborate manner with reference to all his acts and such abstract ideas as death and human worth.

What is there so satisfying in shying stones at a tin can or skipping them across a sheet of water? Small boys do it at every opportunity and it is a joy usually suppressed but rarely completely lost in later life. The thrown stone comes naturally to the hand and the swinging arm, and stones seem made to be picked up and examined, particularly the smooth and glossy pebbles of a beach or gravel bank. We pick them up as soon as we are able to walk and talk, and we picked them up before the first glaciers formed nearly a million years ago. How much earlier we cannot tell but the first signs of man as a tool maker are far older than any trace of human bones we have so far found, and they consist of chipped, split and crudely flaked pebbles found in river terraces of Uganda and other parts of Africa. They take us back to the beginning of the Pleistocene and not only to a time well before glaciers began to form but to a region where they never reached. For while the temperate north fluctuated between glacial ice and considerable warmth, the tropics oscillated between wet and dry and have been warm throughout. Snow in the north was accompanied by rain in the tropics although the early pebble chippers lived long before the first drenching pluvial period arrived, when water was present much as it is now: locally abundant but confined to its courses.

Camps were made beside rivers and lakes in order to obtain water and also to lie in wait for animals coming down to drink. It is an old practice that survives in Africa to this day although the personnel has changed considerably. In such places pebbles and rounded boulders lie ready to the hand and have always done so. The oldest terraces contain pebbles showing no sign of manipulation but those not quite so old contain a profusion of pebbles that are split and trimmed all in a similar way. Natural agencies could never have been so consistent, and the flaked stones most likely were used for skinning game and cutting meat into pieces small enough to be managed by fingers and teeth. The astonishing thing about these pebbles is that they are found in such large numbers, as though they were the product of local factories that stored them up against future needs. Whether this is the way it was, the earliest example of human foresight, or whether the workers got in a rut and didn't know when to stop, technology for its own sake without adequate consumer service, is hard to say.

The same technique used to flake off the edges of pebbles to form a cutting edge passing to a point was employed almost from the beginning to make choppers or so-called hand axes from larger stones, and in nearly all of the early stone industries both flakes and the residual cores were used in the manufacture of implements. Whichever was the main incentive, a valuable by-product was produced and inevitably put to good use. Modern industry is more complex but it works on the same principle. The techniques employed were fairly simple, just as their operators may have been. The simplest was to remove flakes with the aid of a hammerstone and it was used during the earliest phases and for a long time after. Another was to swing a lump of rock against a stone anvil, the block-on-block technique. This led to the invention of the cylinder-hammer technique which first appeared in Europe during the first interglacial period and in Africa during the corresponding inter-pluvial between the first and second deluge. By using the side of a cylindrical hammer of bone or of hard wood, flatter flakes were removed from a large flake or from a core after it had first been blocked out with a hammer stone or on an anvil. The human populations were small but in certain areas stone tools occur in incredible numbers and many of them perfect and unused. I feel sure an artistic pride was taken in the work that drove the stone workers to continue far beyond the immediate need. There is creative satisfaction in carving whether it results in a finely whittled stick, a stone sphinx or a flaked pebble.

The men who made the hand axes or choppers lived in open country in Africa, Europe and Asia and only took to caves at a later time and in certain regions. In tropical climates caves are the homes of bats, scorpions, snakes—a host of creepy, crawly things that I doubt we ever very much enjoyed. Open plains and lake shores where you could see what was coming, whether good or bad, rather than dark forests or darker caves appear to have been the scene of their activity. Moving from place to place according to shifting climates or local circumstances man kept to the pattern of his ways, and insofar as we can measure his progress by the tools he left behind him the most extraordinary thing about him is his astonishing slowness of development. For over half a million years he evolved nothing more elaborate of a tangible more or less permanent nature than flaked stones of one sort or another—the slow perfection of the original invention—and fire. And apart from Pekin man and his somewhat less advanced contemporaries in Java we know almost nothing of the man himself throughout the first long half of the Pleistocene period. When he began to chip his pebbles two or three hundred thousand years before the time of the Pekinese he may already have been very much like them in brain and thought or he may have had quite a way to go. The stones alone suggest that the difference may not have been very great, and that the great surge forwards from the man-ape kind took place early and explosively even before the ice age really started, or at least before it was significantly under way.

Yet one thing is certain. Man has not evolved like a quick-growing shoot thrusting its solitary way up through an established and stable undergrowth. The earth itself has heaved and sighed and all creatures have changed in some degree. The prospective human brain expanded; otherwise we stayed as we were before. Our fellow travelers also moved closer to their modern form though more in terms of brawn and bone than in terms of brain. The late Pliocene was marked by the slow rising of rocky ranges culminating towards the end of the period in the final upward reach of the Himalayas, the Alps and the Cordilleras. Asia was sliced across the middle with cooling steppes to the north and full tropics to the south, while the bridge connecting north and south America rose into place for the first time in forty million years, for the first time since the Eocene when only tarsiods and primitive monkeys were abroad to represent the primates. The high peaks did not alone precipitate the ice age but at least they were an essential contributing cause, and we may have to wait until Everest has worn down to half its present height before we can be sure the ice won't come and come again.

Man appeared as a tool maker during the interval between the attainment of the greatest upfolding by the land and the first coming of the ice sheets. And during that time and throughout the first glacial-pluvial period, at least, the Sahara and Arabian deserts were more or less green and passable. From southeast Africa to southeast Asia a great belt of tropical plains and forests extended south of the central mass of mountains and there is little doubt that newly-formed man ranged freely across the planet within this zone. Apart from the times when the deserts have been dry and impassable the whole belt has been continuously inhabitable throughout the ice age as a whole. Europe and northern Asia on the other hand have been regions available for occupation during the ice-free intervals, while the Americas apparently were out of reach until much later in our history.

If we could go back to these early days when we began to trap or run after big or not-so-big game for our supper we may have found ourselves somewhat strange to look at, with a low forehead in terms of what we now expect to see, with heavy eyebrow ridges giving a formidable beetle-browed effect, and an altogether disconcerting amount of hair, none of which would have disqualified us as being human. How the game would have appeared to us would have depended upon where we were, whether in Africa or in Eurasia. For the period of our transition from flat or low browed to middle browed heads was transitional for the game we chased as well.

Elephants, horses and primitive bison came on the scene at this time; before this their ancestors were less elephantine, less obviously horse, and not so ox-like. We would have known the newcomers for what they were, in spite of a certain unfamiliarity, just as we would have known man even though we might not have cared to shake hands with him. Yet in Africa some of the earlier types survived alongside the new, just as man-apes and man coexisted at least for awhile. Early man knew the three-toed horse as well as the fleeter one-toed beauties we eventually learnt to ride, and he saw giraffes with antlers and short necks as well as the long-necked creatures who now look down upon the world. There were others as well, some old and some new, which he took for granted but we would have found to be strange. Yet gradually but inexorably old kinds gave place to new. Antlered giraffes gave way to longer necks and legs and shorter horns as a fast get-away became a greater asset than a tendency to linger and fight. And as the great beasts grew larger and either faster or more formidable, man became ever more watchful, ever more successful in pitting his wits against mass and power, more and more adept at slipping out of trouble, and as the challenge grew greater so did his brain, for the laggards on both sides got left behind in the race for the future.

By the end of the second wave of ice and rain or shortly after, we find him in the Indonesian tropics and keeping fires going to take the chill out of northern China caves. He is man, as his skulls and his stones have shown us, but he is still not the particular man we are looking for. We come back to our vantage point, for somewhere in the second and enormously long interglacial period, the Great Interglacial, Homo sapiens or someone remarkably like him makes his appearance, perhaps two hundred thousand years ago.

11

NAKED AND TANNED

O N the south side of the river Thames east of London a skull was found in a deep layer of a gravel pit, together with flint instruments and the bones of many mammals of kinds that roamed the earth during the long interglacial period. The flints are hand axes of a more refined sort than those of the Pekin folk. The front part of the skull is missing and so is the face and jaws. It doesn't seem very much to go on, but it all depends on your experience, your point of view and your imagination. The shape of the forepart seems to be dictated by the contour of the larger part we already possess, in the same way that you could draw a complete apple from one that had had a large bite taken out of it. In any case this skull that was found at Swanscombe is a famous one. There is little doubt concerning when its owner lived and there is a decidedly modern cast to it. Some authorities imbued with more caution than others or constitutionally reluctant to allow our present species so great an antiquity say that if we had the rest of the skull it might look very different from our own and that until we do get the rest of it or another one like it we should forget the matter. Others with a greater yearning for a distant past or temperamentally bolder or more impatient say give it the benefit of the doubt, complete the outline the way it seems to go, and since the result is then a modern-looking skull admit the owner and his kind to the rank of Homo sapiens.

Caution can be carried too far, especially when we are short of time and here I think it is a little like refusing to speculate concerning the other side of the moon: is it very much like the side we see or something else entirely? You take your choice and I'll take mine and project from the known to the unknown. I think the skull is modern in all but time itself and we might as well accept the conclusions of the official report on the find. Judging from the thickness of the bone, by careful measurements of critical dimensions, and from the shape of the brain cast made from the skull, the experts announced that the owner was a woman who died in her early twenties, that she had a well-convoluted brain with a total capacity of about 1350 cubic centimeters, and that the brain was lopsided on the right side. That is to say the lady was left-handed, though her habits were probably crude, and she had all the brain she needed to have gone to college had she had the chance and the proper preparations. But she didn't. She kept house in her own way for a man who flaked flints and hunted a queer rhinoceros in an England that was not even an island, and in semitropical heat.

If we walked with our present posture with a full sized head balanced on the top of our neck so long ago, how modern did we look in other ways? Did we grow to maturity as naked as we were born or did we carry a coat of hair like most other mammalian types? At some time in the past our ancestors were thickly covered and at some later time they walked naked upon the land. We still have our head of hair which we presumably never lost, but you cannot tell from a fossil thighbone whether the thigh it supported was furry or delectable to touch. We cannot tell directly when or how we gained our so-called innocence but we can make a guess. It depends somewhat on how we start.

Not so long ago all that was known of ancient man came from European discoveries and inquiries and it was all tied up with the last phase of glacial advance when Europe was under ice or snow. The Neanderthal race occupied this region and appeared to be coarsely built, round shouldered and uncouth with possibly a good coat of hair to keep the cold a little farther from the marrow. He could have been like this but the hairy coat is a conclusion drawn from circumstances and not otherwise supported. On this basis modern man was considered an innovation of more recent descent, and nakedness as we now experience it was thought to be newly won. The question was how? And the only answer was ingenious if not sensible: the cold climate was all too cold for the amount of hairy covering even a Neanderthal may have had, and being a hunter of large game he took to wearing hides for extra warmth; which encouraged the propagation of lice and fleas within his own furry layer to such an extent that he virtually scratched it off. I have no doubt that he scratched, and he may have lost some hair, even where he couldn't reach it himself since the business of 'you scratch my back and I'll scratch yours' goes back as far as monkeys. But his offspring would have been as hairy as ever, for according to Western Science no habits or conditions acquired during the life of an individual are passed on directly through inheritance to his progeny. Your child may be much as you were as a child and may consequently develop the same peculiar turn of mind, but no matter how much I develop my muscles through chopping wood my son will be as flabby as I used to be unless he works as hard. Copy-catting of course is something else and is inheritance through propinquity as distinct from propagation. Only in Russia, and for political and not scientific reasons, is the idea fostered that self-improvements can be passed on by other than social means. So the thought that we lost the hair on our body by rubbing it off might appeal in that quarter. Elsewhere it seems ridiculous.

I believe that when man modernised his head he modernized his body, and that the large selfconscious brain and naked sensitivity came together, although there are two ways of looking at the problem.

Human nakedness intrigues me, as a puzzle, not a prospect. It is potent with meaning, both with regard to our past and to the quality of being human. Is it useful or ornamental or both? We may have acquired it, as Darwin thought, through generations of choosing for mates the least hairy among the possible candidates, with a compensatory taste for long tresses and long beards. Sexual selection of this kind might have produced the nakedness of man, not to mention feminine curves, if there had been any good and persisting reason why a sleek coat of hair should be unpleasing in a well-covered society. I believe it is much more likely that we found ourselves naked and came to like it because there was little else we could do. We all accept what we are born into without any question and prefer the familiar above everything else, although to wait on a street corner and dispassionately watch pale humanity walking by can be a most disheartening experience. Personality is our saving grace, not our shorn and shaven form.

One approach is to ask who goes naked besides ourselves? Elephants and rhinoceros come to mind with a few large mammals which live more or less in water and make comparison difficult. Those of the land are tropical, large and thick skinned; those of the sea are large, thick skinned with blubber all over. Large size and thick skin seem to signify more than living in a hot climate, although during the last ice phase northern species of elephant and rhinoceros had woolly coats; but they died out before the ice melted and those now living in the tropics are the descendants of other kinds. Yet life in the tropics may have had something to do with it, for a large animal, and we rank as such, has much greater difficulty in disposing of its excess heat than a small one and the hotter the climate the harder it is to do so. More than any other time this is when hair gets in the way unless you have an efficient radiator like the tongue and the panting lungs of a dog. Keeping cool under trying circumstances I am sure is part of the story, yet it is far from being all and our nakedness may have been gained in the first place in a somewhat illicit manner.

Naked as the day we were born is a description which fits us throughout our life were it not for the odds and ends we throw over our skin to hide the true state of affairs. Even in the tropics pride or prejudice causes us to clothe our nudity but we all are aware of the masquerade. Lack of cover seems natural enough for the newly born and it is a common condition among the smaller mammals. Many of them are born before hair has had a chance to form, but sooner or later it always comes. Our nakedness is of another kind for we are not born early, we are born late, and a month or two before we are born we do have a fine covering of hair all over. Thereafter, except on the top of the head, and at puberty in other places, the hairy coat gets less and less. Hair normally falls out and is successively replaced by new hair, but over most of our body this does not take place and by the time we are born most of the original coat has already been shed.

What might have been expected we can see in the chimpanzee who bears its young after eight months instead of nine. Shortly before the time of birth the chimpanzee has a light-colored and apparently bare skin except for a thatch of dark hair on its head, almost exactly like many a new-born human. But in the final month the young chimpanzee becomes covered with hair and is born a typically hairy animal. This is the state of affairs among the primates as a whole with man as the only exception. We stand apart not so much in following a different path as in failing to follow the original path through to the end. We not only project our infancy into our later life, we carry our prenatal condition through into childhood and in this particular matter of hairlessness as long as we live. I do not mean that chimpanzees and other apes or monkeys have ever been hairless but that the human-like phase, with regard to hair, that they pass through on the way to greater hairiness is simply a stage in the process—and the stage at which our own hairy development becomes arrested; which suggests that we are not hairless for the sake of being naked but because we have put the brakes on our development as a whole.

We continue to grow and develop but we never quite reach that final state of hairy maturity characteristic of our ancient past and our nearest living relatives. Our nakedness is the symbol of our humanity, for just as the skin remains in this prenatal condition so do we find the prenatal state in other features. The human face with its smooth human skull, apart from sheer size, is as prenatal or fetal a feature as the hairless skin and for the same reason. I have no doubt that unborn man-apes were not unlike our unborn selves, but the growth of the skull slowed down and the skull grew thick while the face went on growing to the size we now feel is monstrous. The head of the man-ape, if it is to be our starting point, must be taken as a whole, for an animal, whether a man or a mite, develops as a whole and not in bits and pieces. I speak here as an embryologist, and professionally since this is my specialty, but I am aware now of the limitations of language. Language has evolved as verbal symbols to convey common familiar experiences among those who converse and we are brought up sharply when we try to describe the completely strange. I have this difficulty now because I am familiar with embryos and you probably are not, although I confess to it mainly because it is a universal human limitation with far-reaching consequences, as we will see. Meanwhile this question of the face and head cannot be ignored. The mechanics of head development in the growing embryo are intelligible but they are not communicable in terms of common speech unless there is a shared familiarity. Yet the essential point is this: that there is a certain staking out of territory in the early embryo during which the general extent of the head is laid out; within this region the brain is staked out first and the facial part somewhat later; if the brain region is not too large, plenty of territory is left for facial constructions; but if a very large brain is to form, a more or less corresponding part of the initial area is set aside for it and what is left for the face and the bony substance of the skull is reduced. The outcome is a small and decidedly fetal type of face and a much thinner skull as consequences of the brain's expansion. The jaws, as distinct from the chin itself, have also become smaller from the same general cause and our wisdom teeth rarely have room enough to erupt and function properly. I have not looked into this but perhaps the less wisdom tooth you have, the better your brain.

Yet we are concerned with more than spatial patterns, for time may be even more important. A brain that is adaptable, that is capable of being educated along new lines by experience or example, must be young. A young brain is one that is still growing, although the rate of growth need be but very low indeed. And inasmuch as a highly intelligent brain must be both fairly large and decidedly adaptable, the longer the delay in attaining the final state the better the brain will be. There has been as much incentive to prolong the later phases of brain growth and differentiation as there has been to grow one larger and larger. Either state would be valuable by itself, but only in combination do you get a brain capable of understanding electronics or the ways of the opposite sex. No wonder we are large, naked and undeveloped at the time of birth.

Moreover there is a very practical side to this business of producing individuals with excessively large brains. The circumstances of birth itself place restrictions on brain size at birth. The head of a baby must be no wider than the pelvic opening of the mother, for otherwise, except in these days of Caesarean section when even siamese twins are unfortunately encouraged to live, both mother and infant die at childbirth. If the brain is to grow rapidly to a larger size than this limitation imposed by the skeleton of the mother, it must postpone much of its growth until after birth—which again brings out the fetus in us all. The biggest brains will be those of infants with their greatest growth yet to come, and such infants are inevitably those that are the most infantile at birth, using the term in its literal and complimentary sense. We have been powerfully constrained to become what we are and primarily we are naked because we could not be otherwise and still have as much brain as we required for survival. Whether we have been forced farther along this road than was absolutely necessary is a very different question, but stranger things have happened and it is far from being clear.

It is one thing to be naked and quite another to be aware of the fact, and there is all the world of difference between being truly self-conscious and being overly sensitive to the size of your image in the eyes of your fellows. I have suggested that we lost most of our hair as an incidental accompaniment of brain expansion, yet to some extent part of this expansion comes directly from the loss of body hair. The naked skin, no longer primarily occupied by hair, has a much greater sensitivity and is generally thinner than the hide we used to have. Sensory nerves for touch and pain and heat and cold abound, each pouring messages into the brain and causing lateral brain expansion by their fibrous presence. Having had a thin naked skin virtually wished upon us somehow we have managed to convert it into a diffuse but highly sensitive receiving apparatus. The meaning of a little draught, a little warmth, a little touch is sensed immediately and general awareness both of our body itself and what goes on around it are brought to a high level. For the mind is alert to the extent that it receives impressions. Remove the stimuli and we go to sleep.

Sometimes it seems to me to have grown to maturity covered, apart from borrowed and expensive substitutes for what nature used to provide for nothing, by only a thin, hairless and extremely sensitive layer of parchment is exposure indeed. I feel vulnerable in too many ways, although to stand in the sun and the breeze after a swim, blowing hot and cold like a living thermometer responding to both heat and humidity, is stimulating. In the long run however it is also limiting. We tend to lump all human beings together and call them mankind but throughout the whole period of their existence they have always been individual men and women, children and babes. And just as I wince under an equatorial sun and shiver at the thought of subpolar climates, I feel sure that my kinfolk of past times avoided both extremes as much as possible and kept to the subtropical lowlands always in search for the happy mean. Not until accumulation of subcutaneous fat conferred a degree of insulation would even temperate zones have been willingly occupied, though whether blubber grew where it was most needed and we came to like it best that way, or whether it grew where we liked it most and thereafter made the best of it is a moot question.

I am also sure that my ancestral skin was brown, but not too dark and not too light. White skin is a defective skin and why white man should be so proud of his pink and white complexion is hard to say. Perhaps at heart we are not too pleased, for no other race seems so anxious to hide its skin from the gaze of others or looks so nude when stripped of clothes. White skin and prudery seem to go together. Certainly a light brown skin is more becoming and generally more efficient. As it is, when white-skinned beauties and other shapes step from the shade into the sun they must be covered with clothing, lotions, wide-brimmed hats and sunglasses. The ten-gallon hat of the Texan is a sign of weakness and his predecessor got along well enough with only a band to keep his hair out of his eyes.

Light warms you, shatters you, and builds you up, particularly the ultra-violet and infra-red which you cannot see. I used to think it was just a sentimental prejudice which made an open fire so much pleasanter than a radiator, quite apart from the bright, colorful and flickering picture it makes. That warm tingling glow, however, that seems to pass right into you is no illusion, for the radiant infra-red rays do pass through the skin to heat the blood itself as it races through the fine vessels lying beneath. Dull-looking radiators merely warm the air and the surface of your skin and leave you coping with cold feet and a hot head almost worse off than you were before. Yet even in the subtropics you can get too much of radiant sun-given heat and a pigment layer at the base of the skin is necessary as a screen.

In these days of covered-up and indoor civilization we dose our children with cod liver oil, usually encapsulated to hide the smell, so that they will have enough vitamin D to build hard bones. We need to do so because of the way we live, not because of the way we are, for ultra-violet light acting at the base of the skin but outside the pigment layer produces the vitamin all the time if given a chance. The horny layer of your skin, which rubs off to some extent after every bath, absorbs the light and puts it to work, although too much light or too thin a skin may be hazardous. Rays that penetrate too deep actually kill the skin so that you peel and burn and become poisoned by your own dead tissues. Only a thick outer layer and dense black pigment gives full protection under the equator or on arctic icefields, but only full blooded Negro races are so well equipped. For the rest of us, the tanning that screens the heat rays also serves to screen black light too, though the vitamin-D factory lies on the outer side of the screen and works so long as light can reach it. So we tan in the sun and bleach in the shade and this goes for all who are light brown, reddish, yellowish, olive or just plain dirty white. Only the pale pinkish Nordics stemming from northeast Europe blush in the full light of day, painfully susceptible to the sun, which suggests an uncommon kind of past.

It's not the heat, it's the humidity, is a statement you often hear, though it's not exactly true. Neither alone is particularly troublesome and it is the combination which makes you pant and sweat. Having inherited a tonic muscle condition that is continually producing internal heat to keep the body warm, there is as much trouble keeping cool as supplying fuel to the furnace. When outside temperatures are below eighty-one degrees you lose heat by radiation and convection from your skin, but higher than that you sweat and evaporate the heat. If the humidity is high you start to drip at ninety-three degrees and had better sit down; in a reasonably dry atmosphere you sweat all over at one hundred and six degrees and had best be careful lest you start to cook. And under these circumstances in a tropical desert you lose half a gallon of water through your skin every hour, half the volume of your blood, though only as long as you can replace it. In any case the strain on your heart is great and sooner or later you are likely to dry out as a dehydrated mass of human meat attractive only to a vulture. So a hunter with primitive weapons will be up before daylight hoping to make his kill while it is yet cool, and an Arab conducting a caravan or herding camels travels by the light of the moon or stars and sleeps under a light-proof tent in the heat of the day. Tropical man, particularly of the open plains, is lean and slender for the sake of keeping cool and only the Eskimo is round and fat for the sake of keeping warm.

12

OLD MORTALITY

A HISTORIAN recently wrote that the past does not exist and what we call the past is our present thinking about what went on before us. The last part of the statement is obviously true, but the first part is like saying that beauty lies only in the eye of the beholder. The word 'only' imposes a restriction I cannot accept for the same reason I cannot accept the thought that the past does not exist other than what is in the conscious minds of the living. It implies that I am only I in the split second of the present, which is no time at all, and that duration has no meaning. If this were so there could be neither symphony nor even melody, neither an organism nor an action. If the universe has a reality in any way corresponding to what our senses tell us, then the past I believe is significant and real quite apart from what I or you or anyone else now thinks about it. It is this attempt to make mental reconstructions of the universe as it is and as it has been, and in such a way that the human organism itself appears as an integral part of it that is uniquely human. Much depends on the way we look at things and the same clues have different meanings for different men. Or a new ingredient or a new method of measuring time or a new technique of analysing ancient deposits may give an entirely new slant to the picture.

So far we have found no more bones than would fill a small closet or a large drawer to represent the prehuman past from the beginning of our mammalian divergence up to the end of the great interglacial period. They are not very much but in a sketchy way they show us something of the drama that has taken place. Traces of unmistakably human types, tantalisingly suggestive, turn up here and there in deposits laid down during the first half of the fluctuating ice age and we have strung them together to make a long and slender line. During this time flints became more intricately and more ingeniously made but the extraordinary thing about our history of these half million years is our astonishing slowness of development. Not until the ice pulls back for the third and last but one time is there any suggestion of a quickening of the pace. Yet when the ice sheets melted leaving tundra, steppe and forest in their place in Europe and northern Asia, when the green pastures of Arabia and the Sahara turned to desert again, man seems once more to be on the move.

Unfortunately for our curiosity the wind driven sands bury the bones of the dead beyond chance of recovery and we can only surmise what may have gone on within these earth-spanning gardens during the pluvial periods when the deserts were brought to bloom. All we know is that at the end of the third ice phase men retreated from the reborn deserts, and farther north, from Europe into Asia, a short heavy-muscled beetle-browed man hunted the huge arctic mammals—the mammoth and the woolly rhinoceros. They did so in fact throughout much of the third and last of the interglacial periods which endured for something like fifty thousand years. These Neanderthal men made more elaborate flint weapons and tools than ever before, faced bitter winds and cold wet winters, cooperated effectively in trapping and chasing their lumbering prey.

By modern standards the Neanderthals were anything but handsome. They had retreating foreheads, but their brains were as large as human brains are supposed to be, while in the spring the Neanderthal youth dallied as much as their rather grim circumstances permitted.

They sheltered in caves wherever possible, as their record shows, and amid the toil of keeping fires burning and dragging the great carcasses, or parts thereof, to the mouths of the caves to be cut up for food, they took stock of life and death. For these were men who are now admitted to our species and so far back as this, fifty to one hundred thousand years ago, the human dead were buried in thought-provoking ways. We cannot say for certain what went on before, but here for the first time is evidence that stands forth like a beacon that man recognized his soul.

The caves held human communities larger than single families. Small societies bound together by shelter and by the glowing warmth of fire bounded by darkness, with powers of speech in spite of rather narrow jaws and heavy jowls, had time and reason for contemplation. Human thought runs on practical economic lines only as long as it has to. When the pressure of urgency is absent, as it must be when night or storm closes in upon you; when the radiance of firelight throws flickering lights and shadows on the walls and on the faces of old and young, the mind relaxes and speaks to mind. Here in the caves the bonds between man and man, as well as man and woman and parent and child, were strengthened and human intercourse as far as speech permitted dwelt more and more on the deep concern of every grown individual with the circumstances of life and above all with the ravages and impact of death. The Neanderthal people were uncouth to say the least, they may even have sported a hairy coat like the mammoth and rhinoceros which they hunted, and I am sure that on the surface we would have found them to be repulsive. But they buried their dead.

A man and a child have been found whose bodies had been protected by stones, particularly the heads so that the weight of earth would not crush them; a pillow of flint chippings supported the head of a youth; graves were dug close to hearth fires, and stone tools, meat and red ochre were placed in them beside the dead. And the homes of the dead, as in life, were the rock-shelters and the caves. Death usually came swiftly from violence, accident, more slowly from disease, starvation or exposure, very rarely from old age—it was something that happened or was done to the victim in the same way that a rhinoceros died in a trap at the hands of men. Yet they gave their dead warmth and weapons and food. For what?

Imagination works but feebly even now after perhaps one hundred thousand years of thought upon the subject. We think according to our culture and language in ways distinctly our own and it is difficult to see the world and man through the eyes of the unsophisticated. The primitive mind depends mainly on unity of feeling rather than on logical rules which draw clear lines of distinction between one kind of thing and another. Life is felt to be an unbroken whole with no insurmountable barriers between different spheres and anything and everything can be turned into anything else. Above all, the past, present and future blend into each other, and all nature is one great society of life. I see no reason to suppose that the early Neanderthals were very different in their outlook from that of the primitive and isolated Australian aborigines who still flake stones, daub their bodies, and behave towards death in much the same old way. There is no conception here of immortality of the soul, neither in the Australian nor, by the same token, in the

Neanderthal. Immortality in this sense we use the term accepts the fact of death, and that is exactly what is rejected. Instead we find the strongest and most energetic affirmation of life anywhere in the whole human culture. The spirit of the dead is the spirit of the living. There is no difference, only appearances have changed, and burial rites throughout human times show a struggle between fear of the spirit and the deep desire to retain or recall it. Thus the living are left in a quandary between wanting to nourish and hold the personality they still feel as a living presence, and the difficulty in checking any mischief that invisible hands may incline to do. So the spirit is kept contented and close to home but is essentially hamstrung so that it cannot walk about.

So bodies were buried in the extreme flexed position of a man squatting asleep, tightly bound with thongs to prevent the dead from walking. It is not long since we ceased to scatter ashes behind a hearse along the road to the grave to prevent the ghost from finding its way back to the house. We close the eyes of the dead for the same forgotten reason. Yet always men have drawn a distinction between the desirable and undesirable ghosts, between those who died in a manner unbecoming and those whose presence is beneficial and beloved. Death by violence has always been shocking and the spirits of those who were killed by wild beasts, or killed as outcasts by other men, or of women who died in childbirth were above all to be feared and kept away, for such deaths were ominous. The thought seems to haunt some of us even yet. The criminal, the suicide and the unmarried mother rarely attain to burial in consecrated ground and it used to be that they found their lonely rest at country crossroads, a practice that was an outcome of an older compromise. Ancient Teutonic peoples of Europe often built their altars at crossroads, still a common place for shrines, but their religion involved human sacrifice which always raised the minor question as to who should be sacrificed. Being human and therefore naturally inclined to expediency, they chose their victims mainly among convicted criminals and the sacrifice did double service as an execution. With the coming of Christianity the sacrifice was dropped, but murderers and suicides continued to be buried at the crossroads at dead of night in order to assimilate their funeral to that of the pagans. The sacrificial altar survived in an equally sinister form as the gallows at the crossroads, rarely without a man hanging at the end of the rope to be cut down and buried beneath it.

Among primitive peoples, whether ancient or modern, much as in our own civilized sentiment, death does not make a person cease to belong to his social unit and the living and the dead are simply two classes not unlike the young and the old. And as the old may be feared because of supposedly magical powers, such as those of a witch, or respected for their wisdom, so the dead have been regarded in various ways. All dead as such are terrible because death is contagious and where one violent death occurs others usually follow. They must be controlled, though burial alone may not be enough, for some dead are powerful and must be propitiated, while others may be reborn into the community. If to be reborn then only the good dead are wanted, particularly those of forceful and beneficial personalities, and certain of the dead may for a while become worshipful ghosts. Some one ancestor may in fact so combine in his own personality all the worshipful qualities a good ancestral ghost should have, or some one outstanding quality, that the ghost becomes a god. There is almost nothing an ancestral spirit may be called upon to do or to grant or to avert, generally as an intermediary between living men and the true gods. The older god becomes more remote and the more recent dead must intercede.

Ancestor worship, in various forms of emancipation, spread across the face of the earth, through Africa, Asia and the

Pacific, and was practiced by Greek and Roman alike, by the Vedic Indians of older times and by the Chinese and Japanese to this day. Out of it came Halloween or All Hallows Eve, for the Celtic peoples celebrated the last day of October as the end of the old year and made ready for the new, danced in masks and queer dress from dusk until dawn and conceived more than a New Year alone. But during the night the dead souls walked. In remote parts of Ireland October thirty-first is still the Vigil of Saman, harking back to the Druidic custom of calling together certain wicked souls by Saman, the Lord of Death. But all souls walked, not just the wicked, and the good dead were called upon to help the living.

Candles symbolise the sun, and in the mountainous country of the Tyrol the "Soul lights" are placed on tables to guide the spirits wandering through the darkness of the Black Forest. But in Sicily the children put their boots on doorsills ready for the beloved dead in white robes and soundless feet to come and fill them with gifts. But when the year's end was shifted to late December, to the winter solstice when the sun is weakest, a white-haired, white-bearded man still came at night, soundless and stealthy, to fill boots or stockings with gifts. No one has seen him but every child in Christendom hopes to see him and leaves cake and drink for him to take.

Interment has been always a problem, as we with our padded caskets, slumber rooms, twisted flowers, canned music, and green-lawn cemeteries ought to know, but the one I would have chosen had I lived in another time and had the choice would have been in South America seven or eight thousand years ago, when a man was buried sitting in the huge carapace of a giant extinct armadillo. Majesty must have lived in a death so compounded, and nothing stood in the way of nature reclaiming her own. Yet for the finest and oldest communal cemetery we go much farther back than this, far into the period of the last ice advance. Neanderthal man had mysteriously disappeared and new, taller and thinner-skulled men had taken his place. They also hunted the mammoth. For in Central Europe where the paths of great beasts converged in the Moravian gates an oval grave contained twenty skeletons buried in squatting position, dug beneath an old rock shelter, and enclosed by a fence of mammoth shoulder blades. Somehow it suggests defiance both of death itself and its agent of destruction.

When the dead are magical and feared, trussing them however tightly is no assurance they will not break their bonds, and another method, or so it seems, was used to hold their spirits in their place. Most people, whether primitive or otherwise, feel that the human spirit resides, if anywhere, in the head rather than in the heart or liver. A head may be buried without a body with a certain satisfaction, but a headless body signifies little, not even in a grave. And when the head is regarded as the person, all that is necessary to keep everything under control is to bury the head, and the head alone, in the proper place. Even Neanderthal had an inclination to indulge in this form of security, although his successors, some of them at least, carried the practice to a fine art. In a remarkable cave burial in Bavaria the severed heads of the dead were placed one by one into two scooped out nests in the earth, six in one and twenty-seven in the other, all wearing rich ornaments of deer teeth and shells, sprinkled with red ocre, and all facing west toward the setting sun. Charred remains nearby suggest that the bodies were cremated. You can read many things into this, none with certainty but all together indicating feeling, sensitivity and as great imagination as any that we lay claim to.

Yet the beliefs underlying such a practice when taken literally have been responsible for a queer human trait. If you believe that the spirit of a man resides in his head you may, perhaps, bury his head alone, with reverence or affection, but when the head is that of an enemy it becomes another matter. In taking a head the spirit within is captured and a collection of heads adds to the general stock of spirit or soul matter belonging to a community, and so contributes to the fertility of the human population. Head hunting, like cannibalism, is in essence a religious practice, complimentary to the victim even if not enjoyed by him, and both survive with us symbolically in lockets of hair and sacramental wafers.

Men have been different races in different places for a long time, though the races themselves have changed and they have continually flowed from one region to another. An old practice in one area becomes a new one far away from the centre of the cult, while each and all tend to change as time goes on. In any case burial in the old flexed position, which survives in Australia to this day, was the practice in Egypt until the First Dynasty a little more than three thousand B.C. Bodies were buried with the flesh directly in contact with the hot dry sand, with the result that they dried out quickly and decay was arrested. Yet one of our more distinctive qualities, which we share to a great extent with monkeys, is our inability to leave things well enough alone. Bodies became natural mummies in desert graves only so long as they were simply buried in the sand, but when with all the best intentions to help the dead to live they were enclosed in coffins, the trapped air induced corruption to intervene.

Yet for three thousand years Egyptians made every effort to arrest decay and to perpetuate the identity of the deceased, at least in the case of the small minority who had anything to say on the subject. The thought that the spirit lingered within the flesh and that the dead lived in a most literal sense prevailed and dominated, and by the time of the twenty-first dynasty, about 1000 B.C., the art of making a mummy out of the remains of a man reached its peak. Brains and internal organs were extracted. Mud and sand were forced beneath the skin to plump the body into better shape, red ochre covered the body, and rouge the cheeks and lips, to give them the color of life; and crystal eyes replaced those of the dead. When all was finished the dead man was made, by means of a complicated ritual, to see, hear, talk and eat—a kind of coercive resurrection. Moreover the practice spread far and wide, for mummies were made in the Egyptian style down almost to the last detail in the islands of the Torres Straits between Australia and New Guinea, and until just a few years ago.

Yet throughout the time of the Old Kingdom, during the first centuries when the pyramid builders waxed and waned, the tightly contracted posture of the dead gradually loosened until finally full extension is reached and the body at last lies straight, with its head to the north and its face towards sunrise.

The gradual stretching out of the body suggests both a lessening of the fear that the departed will return to do mischief and the thought that the spirit goes on a journey, as though the living dead were more concerned with continuing life in their own way than hanging around with too much time on their hands. Egyptians are a cheerful, merry people in spite of economic circumstances, and the tomb itself, whether simple or grandiose, arose apparently as a passionate desire to deny the existence of death. On the walls of many tombs the dead speak to the living: "Oh ye living upon earth, who love life and hate death." There was an idea of a sort of temporary resurrection when by means of spells the dead if they liked could come forth from the tomb by day; and an idea that the dead lived with the gods, especially those of the dark underworld, and accompanied the dead sun on his nightly rounds of his realm. It may have been dark but it was far from being hell and the funeral ships of the Pharaohs proclaim opportunity to voyage upon the water as they did upon the Nile when alive. In much later times far to the north, later according to calendar rather than by custom, the early Vikings also sent their royal dead on their journey aboard a ship, the ship usually being drawn up on land or occasionally sent burning out to sea. But they went with all the necessities kings could want: arms, ornaments, horses, and slaves. The dead were launched into an invisible world with all that they might need but freed from the shackling body, for the bodies were cremated to liberate the spirit.

Cremation, almost a sanitary necessity in tropical lands and widely practiced in India, has had a curious history. From the time of the Neanderthal through the long last phase of the ice age well into post glacial times, burial of flexed bodies, or of heads alone, prevailed across the earth, surviving in the Australian sanctuary even now. When the dead still lived but couldn't be left lying around in disintegrating fashion above the ground, what else could you do but put them in a hole in the ground? Even if you had progressed with your thoughts to regard the spirit of the dead as being hampered by the body rather than a part of it, you still could do little but go through the old routine. Cremating the body and burying only the head was a sensible compromise which discarded the trash but hung on to the essentials. The final step of complete cremation necessarily had to wait until something could be done with the ashes besides scattering them to the winds or losing them in the soil, for while the spirit had need to be free, it still needed to take its departure in an unhurried and orderly manner, to take its bearings one way or another.

Cremation in fact had to wait until pots could be made to put the burned bones in, and pottery came into being for the first time during the neolithic revolution which followed close upon the last melting of the great ice sheets. When nothing like pots or urns, other than vegetable gourds and calabashes, had previously been seen upon the face of the planet, it is no wonder that they became objects of the greatest admiration and value. What could be more fitting in every way than to reduce the dead body to its charred remains, easing the escape of the living spirit, putting the compact residue in the most beautiful man-made creation yet to appear, and burying the neat package in the earth?

Throughout the Bronze age, when metals were just coming into use in place of stone, the peoples living near the heart of the world, in Moravia, Bohemia, Hungary and Silesia practiced cremation to the exclusion of all else, so that whole of the Hungarian plain, for instance, eventually became covered with urn fields: cemeteries containing urns with cremated bones, together with accessory vases. Typically the urn or ossuary consisted of two cones base to base, with a hole for the escape of the ghost, for the spirit was to be set free, not bound to the earth unnecessarily. In England urns with their ashes, buried either in barrows or urn fields are common throughout the south. The iron age people whom Caesar found still buried their cremated dead in urn fields, while the Romans themselves a little later followed a similar custom, often putting the burnt remains in a beautiful green glass jar placed in a brick chamber and the whole covered with a great mound of earth. When the Saxons came they continued the same general practice, though with details of their own.

As a general custom cremation came to its untimely end partly as the result of the early Christian Church which taught that the body, or whatever was left of it, had to be reclaimed on the day of judgment, and that it should lie buried with its feet to the east to give the dead a good start when the last trumpet blew; which seems to combine a fuzzy imagination with an element of sunworship. But except in northwest-Europe, which has always been late in receiving ideas and races from southeastern sources, the passion for cremation and the use of urns had already abated before the Christian era began. Until urns were made to contain the ashes, no respectable cremations could be carried out. Once urns were available the new custom spread almost like wildfire and lasted throughout the relatively short bronze age into the age of iron. Smelting and working metals became the fashionable craft and coinciding with the upsurge of metal work, pottery making went into a decline, in quantity but especially in quality, and crematory practice declined accordingly. It was old fashioned and you could no longer get urns as readily and as well made as they used to be. Diversionary interests on earth and the distant sound of a heavenly trumpet put an end to cremation in Christian lands until its revival in our own time.

It seems a pity. Cremation and urn burial was sanitary and neat and much less barbarian than our present practice. For myself, when I am dead, I would prefer to be a skeleton than the most nicely embalmed cadaver and I would sooner be ashes than either. Early man believed in the continuation of life in association with the buried body, as primitive peoples do yet, but he progressed from binding spirit and body together to burning the flesh to set the spirit free. We who say we believe in immortal souls should stand by our conviction and give wings to the spirit instead of making shrouds of lead and canopies of granite. We are more earth-bound in some ways than our ancestors.

13

BEAUTY AND THE BEAST

H AVE you ever sat across from some rugged character or watched a high diver start his fast and graceful fall and thought to yourself 'I wish I could draw'? It comes to most of us at times and with good reason. In some subtle way the mind's eye picks out the essential features or the dynamic sweep of action and urges the hand to follow it and pin it down. Cartoonists catch it at once in a few weighted lines and show you the gist of it, usually exaggerated to drive it home; while the greatest artists with an all-revealing economy of line, paint or stone, place the essence of what they see before you. Few of us can make the hand obey in such a faithful way but we all see beyond and below the surface to some degree, and most unspoiled children know great art when they see it. Before the greatest we stand mute and still, in instant and affirmative acknowledgement. Such communion is worship from the depths of the human soul; religion and the sense of beauty are in fact so interwoven that no matter how far back we attempt to trace them they remain inseparable, the unpredicted and unpredictable insight that has grown from sight and mind. And like a song heard in the night, the earliest human art grew in darkness, potent with the meaning and the needs of life, not two thousand years ago but twenty thousand. On the larger scale of time this is recent enough, yet it puts man the artist right into the middle of the last phase of ice. The last interglacial period drew to its end, the ice thickened and spread for the fourth time, although with several hesitant withdrawals when somewhat milder climates prevailed; and in the first of these we find that the Neanderthalers have gone from the scene and a new race with longer legs and a thinner skull has taken his place throughout Europe and northern Asia. These are our own kind of people and not just relatives we might have viewed with a certain amount of dismay, and they exhibit an energy and a creativeness that foreshadow all that has happened since.

When Neanderthalers were flourishing in their own limited way in Europe and elsewhere, their cousins on the southern borders of the Mediterranean appear to have had a harder time, for deserts were deserts and heat was intense. When the ice finally came in the north the Neanderthalers could not cope with it and disappeared. But the same ice brought rain to the south and along the North African and northern Arabia the land grew green, and new-style man undoubtedly grew more abundant. A few skulls have been found to show that at least he was there and probably had been all along in smaller numbers. In any case North Africa apears to have been the springboard for invasion. The men of the south spread to other lands, possibly to the east by way of Asia Minor but almost certainly to the north into Europe by way of Tunis and Sicily. When ice caps form, water is withheld from the oceans and the sea level falls, and when the ice was thickest the sea level was close to six hundred feet lower than it now is and the channel between Tunis and Sicily narrowed to about forty miles. Land could be seen across the water from Tunis just as the coast of Spain could be seen from Morocco, although no amount of polar ice could have narrowed the channels more than this, let alone have made a land bridge to walk upon. So if these were the routes by which the north was invaded, mankind was already journeying by sea and must have had boats of a kind.

Whatever the means by which they came across, we get the impression now of a new aggressive spirit,—'of taking arms against a sea of troubles'—with a sweep of action and imagination never before expressed and, to my mind, never surpassed. Whatever the pressures behind them or the incentives that drew them on, this phase of the human venture quickly assumed a trans-continental scope ranging from the Pyrenees to Siberia and beyond, for men became so attached to the mammoth and other large mammals that they followed them wherever they went.

Here I believe we have the first clear-cut evidence of men actually invading climatic zones to which they were not adapted, instead of merely adjusting to pleasant or unpleasant circumstances as they arose. Until this time, it seems to me, the early human races evolved in this or that direction according to what was happening to them. Now for the first time mankind is something which happens to the planet, in a small way admittedly compared with our present inclination to meddle with as much of the solar system as we can, but nevertheless as an intrusive spirit.

Tundra and rolling grasslands stretched across Europe and Asia from the Atlantic to the Pacific, lying between the Scandinavian ice cap and the glacial ridge that ran from the Pyrenees across the Alps to ranges farther east, at least during the less severe intervals within the last glacial period. No forests stood in the way, for it was much too cold, but mammoths, bison, horses, stag, reindeer and other creatures ranged from one end of the great belt to the other. And during the severe winters great hordes swept south through the Moravian gates to graze on the Danubian plain where conditions were somewhat milder, pouring back each spring to the more extensive pastures to the north. Of course not all of them did so, particularly those in the western part of the European peninsula, but at the Moravian gates where the glaciers forced the migrating hordes to traverse a narrow passage the bones of more than a thousand mammoths have been found in one large man-made collection. Men camped within the gates and slew the great beasts as they lumbered along, by means of pits and throwing-spears. They made exquisite tools with none of the earlier crudity, and we find bone, horn, antler and ivory used as well as stone. The whole extent of Europe became a vast arena with humanity penetrating the soft underbelly, to steal a phrase, at various times from North Africa and from human stock in the Caspian basin far to the southeast, all contending for meat.

Bone yards became an inexhaustible stock room in which all kinds of tools were to be found ready for use and from which could be drawn unlimited material for improving upon what nature provided. Flints were flaked with razor-edges, capable of carving bone and ivory as well as flensing carcases. It was I think inevitable, since a man has two hands and a curious tendency to tinker, that flints should be used to shape bone and to put shapes on to bone, and that before long the same flints, shaped as engraving tools, should be used to cut designs in rock as well as bone. Hands and eyes combined at first to make a man an opportunist, then a craftsman, and in the end a creative artist.

Of all the works of early man none so stirs the imagination as the art that is to be seen in the caves of France and northern Spain. It takes several forms: finger tracing, engraving, bas-relief, full sculpture and painting, all done on the cave walls. In addition a great deal appears on fragments of bone, ivory and stone. All of it falls within the period lying between the time of greatest severity of the last ice sheet and its final melting, and within this period archeologists recognise an early widespread Aurignacian craft which extended from the Pyrenees to Central Europe and points east, and a later flowering which grew out of it in western France and nearby Spain: the Magdalenian.

Every form of art reflects the culture of the people who created it, and not merely of the individual creative artist himself who can work only within the framework of his particular society, which makes most of so-called modern art seem somewhat ominous. We can do well however to look closely at these late ice-age folk, at their arts and crafts, their religion and their customs, and where their travels took them. We can look at the paintings and carvings simply as art, and one of the foremost art critics of our own time has ranked the best of them as great. If this were not so I doubt whether we would see printed so many fine reproductions of the multicolored, modelled paintings of the cave wall bison.

We take it for granted when we look at something that what we see is exactly what is there. Yet this is only partly true, for while the impression we get may be valid it is far from being the whole truth. A man blind from birth who finally recovers his sight sees only blurred shapes and colors. His eyes may be as good as yours but it takes a long time before he sees that an orange is round or that a tree or a letter have a certain shape, and vision of this sort may never come. For shape is something seen in the mind and it comes as much from action of the eyes as it does from retinal images. You can test this readily: look at any simple object such as an apple or even Eve and, if you are quick enough, you will sense that your eyes have performed a fast run around, tracing the outline for your information. When things are already very familiar hardly a trace of this may be necessary, if any at all, since memory images partaking both of sight and action are evoked in a flash. But if what you are looking at is completely strange to you, either because it is new or because you yourself are pretty new, you have to study it for a considerable time before you feel you have captured it. You follow its lines and contours with rapid movement of the eyes together and you also give the surface the full attention of the retinal center where vision is most acute, by roving over the area in a corrosive fashion for details of texture, color and shade. Seeing is not passive, memories of things seen are more than patterns of remembered light, and when you need to communicate what you have seen you are called upon to select the significant from the less significant. Selection of the meaningful from a host of distractive detail is the essence of true vision, both when attention is first given to the images and when at a later time memory is drawn upon. Here are the roots of all visual art, and we find the whole emergent process in the records of the late ice age people of Europe. We should perhaps distinguish between them and regard the earlier Aurignacian culture as the mammoth age and the later Magdalenian as the product of the reindeer age, although the one more or less grades into the other. Yet the distinction is useful, for hunting mammoth and bison was a little like hanging on to the tail of a tiger, whereas reindeer ranged less widely and demanded less endurance on the part of the hunters.

Pictorial art was undoubtedly from the first both expressive and decorative, the one being a matter of impulse and the other of recognition, but I feel sure that the primary urge was the need to communicate. Language, we must remember, depends not only upon development of voice and articulation and the associated speech control center of the brain, but also upon a memory of sound symbols representing things and actions. And one of the most difficult tasks a human being is ever required to do is to describe clearly and succinctly in vocal or written speech something with which his audience is not familiar. Clear verbal communication demands clear thought and an adequate vocabulary, and always when thought is new we find that language fails. And in so far as languages have grown like any other skills involving extensive memory, there is little doubt that early men had great difficulty in explaining what a bison looked like to a younger generation who had yet to see one. One good diagram avoids a wealth of confusing explanation, and this I believe was the motive underlying the original development of these ancient artistic enterprises, although the initial discovery that you could scratch bone with flint and make lines that suggest something you have seen must have come first.

So it is that the earliest efforts so far found are engravings consisting of meandering parallel lines and poorly drawn outlined figures of animals, made on pieces of bone. Throughout most of the mammoth age the bodies of animals are shown in profile with the head full face and only two legs represented. This is as true of the cave paintings of the period as it is of the portable bone portraits, except that the human hand is added to the picture, either as a positive print filled in with color or a negative one as though a hand was held against the wall and the color painted around it. The hand could be the earliest signature, as a thumb print may be even now, but it is much more likely to have been symbolic—the human hand with all its capacity for deadly action placed close to a recognizable graphic symbol of the intended victim. In general the art of the mammoth age remained crude, but vigorous, which its people most certainly were. Their most striking creation however was in the form of sculptures representing the human female figure—a small stone Venus, bulging all over with fertility or maternity, carved from limestone and found from one end of Europe to the other and possibly in Russia as well. They are the first tangible indication that humans were as consciously aware of the mystery and overwhelming import of birth as well as death. The figurine for birth, the mammoth for life, and bones buried with red ochre and ornaments for the living dead symbolise these hardy hunters. Moreover they drew the sign of the swastika, probably to symbolise the sun.

In following through the history of any people we nearly always find that we have one sequence of events which holds for the central, home, region of their culture and another which represents their dispersion into distant regions. The mammoth men of western Europe, during a period of ten or more thousand years, evolved the advance of culture of the reindeer age, although a great ebb and flow of humanity occurred throughout the period. But while this was going on, other communities of mammoth hunters, in particular those who followed mammoth and bison into Siberia, continued to follow their giant prey to the ends of the earth. This is a departure which takes us far from the cave art of the Pyrenees in more senses than one, but the great deficiency of language is its serial nature in which one word follows another to give an essential linear dimension. Life and the universe are not like that. Everything happens at once but you can neither speak nor write that way, and I find myself restricted by another of our human limitations. It is well that we should know them.

Mammoths, like the closely related elephants and the not-so-closely related mastodons of equal size, ranged across the tundra of Europe and Asia. Each time the ice caps formed and the sea level dropped, the shallow shelf at Bering Strait became dry land, and at the commencement of the last ice phase, if not before, mammoths and mastodons crossed the bridge and plodded their heavy way south as far as the Andes. Nor did they travel alone, either into the Americas or anywhere else. Saber toothed tigers accompanied them, preying on them whenever possible, and where the tigers went men went too. For they were hunting mammoths and mastodons in the Americas at least as far south as Mexico ten or eleven thousand years ago when the ice cap was about to melt, for spear points and flensing tools have been found in close association with mammoth remains. But altogether the evidence indicates that such hunting was already long established in the western hemisphere and that mammoth hunters crossed into North America at least as soon as they are known in Central Europe. No glaciers blocked their way across the Bering bridge. Cold climate they were already used to, and a relatively mild migration route along the whole of the Pacific coast from Siberia to Central America lay open to them when the strait was closed.

To what extent they wore garments made from the skins of animals we can only surmise, but at some stage along the way mammoth hunters invented or discovered the bone safety pin for pinning together their robes and the chances are that those that made the long trek through Siberia and down the Pacific belt of the Americas had at least this minimum equipment. Whether they had stone lamps such as the Eskimos use is another matter, but it is possible, as we shall see.

Although the American mammoth hunter seems to have left us little more than evidence of his existence and of his success in slaying mammoths, the mammoth hunters of western Europe turned more and more to reindeer and bison. Perhaps the toll they had taken of mammoths became too big, or perhaps bison and reindeer herds more than made up in aggregate what the less gregarious mammoths offered in accessible meat. In any case the resident human population that occupied southern France from the Spanish Pyrenees to the Swiss Jura, with reinforcement and some displacement from the south and east, became progressively the master of their surroundings and far less inclined to track the plodding foot prints of heavy pachyderms. Tools manufactured by them from bone, ivory, antler or horn were beautifully made, and so were the fine-eyed bone needles they finally employed in making garments. It is not customary to speak of a bone-age people, but if there ever was a bone age this was it.

If it were not for bone engravings I doubt if we could correlate the cave wall art with any particular phase of the associated human culture, but as it is cave drawings can be matched with bone drawings for style and subject; and inasmuch as bones and other pieces of portable art are found buried with flints and other indications of the cultural level, and are clearly older than anything that lies above them and younger than what lies beneath, the sequence of changes is fairly well known.

The oldest true paintings of animals are in simple areas of color, sometimes no more than colored outlines in red, yellow or black not unlike the earliest of the rock engravings. Yet before long the assurance of the artist becomes more apparent and the rudimentary silhouettes become progressively more precise and more refined, until at last they become vigorous and very true to life. Important diagnostic details like the cloven hoof of the ox and deer family are always clearly shown. In one style found in the caves of eastern Spain the rock engravings become much finer, with the whole body filled in with fine lines—a little less naturalistic perhaps but none the less vigorous. In one development the outline of the animal is discontinuous, consisting of short parallel dashes at an angle to the outline, indicating hair. In another long parallel striations represent hair but cleverly arranged to suggest shading as well. Sculptures and reliefs are also known which belong to the first phase of Magdalenian progress, with details such as horns, nostrils and hoofs if necessary painted on. Pigments were obtained from natural deposits of red iron oxide, yellow to orange iron carbonates, blue-black oxide of manganese, and the black charcoal of burnt bones. Raw color was pounded and mixed with fat and bone paint tubes and stone palettes have actually been found associated with the caves. And since the dark recesses of the caves were as dark in those ancient days as they are now, the paintings could be neither made nor seen without a light. Lamps were necessary then as now, and, more surprisingly, they have been found: stone lamps similar to those still used by Eskimos, with carbonaceous matter still within them indicating animal fat as fuel and perhaps some kind of moss as wick. Animal skulls were also used for the same illuminating purpose.

Whatever the underlying motive may be, art in general seems to follow a certain sequence which is as true of the cave art as of any other kind. Early unskilled efforts give place to skilled and vigorous portrayals indicating both a mastery of the medium and a keen penetrating observation of the subject. Then all too often painting or drawing seems to be conducted for its own sake without much thought given to the nature of things portrayed, and in the second phase of Magdalenian cave art the engravings retain their skill but show a falling off in vigor, while the paintings show great degeneration. The fine shaded paintings of the first phase are replaced by poor flat-wash silhouettes, a sloppy process of filling in an engraving with color. Anatomical detail is still noted but is less naturalistic. In the final phase however the cave art finds its full flowering in the many colored idealistic paintings of bison and deer—far from the original naturalistic perfections but capturing and expressing in a clearly recognizable form something of the very essence of the animal concerned. Instead of being a particular bison or a certain individual deer or horse or goat or even lion, the paintings represent bison or deer in a strikingly symbolic form.

It seems to me we have two mysteries here: the significance

of the engravings and paintings with reference to the place in which they are found, and the meaning of the progressive change from fumbling naturalistic drawing to stylized abstract painting. Both express the mind of man, and I see no essential difference between my own and the mind of the reindeer and mammoth people of ten to twenty thousand years ago. All that has changed is what we put into it, not the thing itself, although the earlier state being less cluttered may be easier to understand.

The progression from clumsy inaccurate drawing all the way through faithful representation of form and detail, to final abstraction, is very much the course followed by an individual artist during his own development and maturation. Not that all hopeful artists complete the course and too many I think endeavor to attain the art of leaving out before they have acquired the ability of putting in. Futhermore, I think the statement you often hear that 'seeing is believing' is one of the most misleading ones a man has ever made, for you are more likely to see what you believe than believe what you see. To see anything as it really exists is about as hard an exercise of mind and eye as it is possible to perform, and the initial difficulty expressed in early phases of cave men's art and in the early efforts of any other would-be artist is as much the fault of the mind's eye as it is of the hand that tries to draw. The eye itself soon learns to convey adequate information concerning shapes, in addition to color and texture, and the hand readily gains steady control of an inscribing tool. The main difficulty is mental and what we see in the progressive development of cave wall art is the progressive change in the way human beings looked at things.

At several sites thousands of engravings on bone have been found of the kind only beginners would make, suggesting something of the nature of a school of instruction, but once a certain degree of manual skill was acquired, and wall engravings were made, the nature of the drawing becomes informative. The early ones are for the most part outlines, in black or color, with at most a few significant lines enclosed. In a sense they are silhouettes, yet not only are they instantly recognisable for what they are, whether bison, goat, wild pig, horse, deer or mammoth, or perhaps one of the large birds such as crane, duck, goose, owl, partridge and swan, but they convey either action itself or the frozen immobility of a startled animal in the presence of man. You are impressed by the feeling that the animal before you is suddenly alert or already moving in panic, and it seems obvious that the human eyes that gazed on the living scene were watching intently, following every curve and projection of the animal's shape and above all tense in anticipation of its prospective flight. In one instance a herd of reindeer is exquisitely indicated by one animal more or less in complete outline, with a forest of antlers behind it—the actual impression you would get if you were keeping your eyes on one although conscious of the rest.

It was this that the mind carried back to inscribe on bone and later perhaps to copy on to the wall of the cave. Outlines in action express the eyes and mind of the hunter. Then and only then, as familiarity with the subjects increase and, building on the graphic foundations laid by past generations, the third dimension complete with superficial texture is added to the outlines. The animals become subsantial either in full or partial relief or by means of shading or color modelling, and you receive the fine detailed information you might have gained from studying a dead animal. There is in fact a loss of vigor which suggests that the artists are no longer the hunters, and that they were more aware of the visual information gained from a steady contemplation of the animal rather than an active mental participation of the creature's intent or action. Focussing movements of the eyes and retinal image analysis come to the fore, and there comes a time I think when the mind with its memory becomes over-crowded with small though related facts. Then it is that abstraction begins again, this time from the welter of informa-tion within the memory instead of the composite complex-ity of an original scene. Subconsciously the mind selects the more significant and tends to discard the less, and as it does so insight is experienced at the conscious level. And so it was that the later phase of cave art emerged as a stylised and strong portrayal of what the animal had come to mean. The paintings finally symbolise the animals in a powerful way that leaves a much deeper impress in the mind of the observer than either the detailed substantial pictures and sculptures of the middle phase or the dynamic outlines of the first. Ab-straction, symbol-making and insight have grown together.

Why did the mammoth and reindeer hunters go to so much trouble to draw, carve or paint portraits of animals so far in the dark difficult recesses of caves where they could be seen only by the light of a lamp and where no man ever lived? It was certainly not art for art's sake, nor was much of it even decorative, for all too often one effort is engraved on top of another in anything but a pleasing manner. With the excep-tion of the lion, all the animals figured are those that were hunted as food, and the lion being a cave lion was undoubt-edly hunted of necessity when it wandered in or out of caves sacred to man. Ceremony and ritual were undoubt-edly involved, and in the later times men who may have been artists or sorcerers or both probably formed a distinct class. How else can you interpret a stone pulpit, twelve feet from the ground and entered from behind, with the cave wall be-side it carrying the image of a man masked with the antlers of a stag or bearing the tail of a bison or horse?

Here is your original devil, complete with horns and tail, the master of a dark and terrifying underworld lit only by the flickering light of flame, with the fluttering shadows of frantic bats adding to the general effect. The whole picture has become that of the devil in hell, which is a pity since originally it was the hope of all mankind or at least of all who lived in the great hunting zone of Eurasia. You need to project yourself into this world of the past to get the feeling. How intense and vital the living reality must have been, as it was felt, thought and experienced at the time, is shown I think by the very fact of survival of the all-too-vivid and influential myth of his satanic majesty ruling in a dark, flaming and fearful netherworld, waiting for the souls of men. For here is nothing less than the early religion of man, incorporated in a twisted and discredited form in later beliefs surviving even now in certain fundamentalist Christian sects.

When I was younger and less inclined to consider the immanence of falling rock and all the other treacherous dangers of sliding through dark underground water-carved passages in the limestone hills of southwest England, I found myself sitting at the long dead hearth of the people who, judging from the bones mixed in with the charcoal of their kitchen, hunted giant reindeer and knew the sabre-toothed tiger. They left no drawings or paintings on the walls, or if they did the rocky walls have collapsed like so much of the cavern roofs, but they left the ashes of their fires, their tools, a few of their own bones and at least one skull, and I found it all too easy to drop back in time some ten thousand years. In each such place you descended from an old river gorge through a wide or narrow passage into a spacious cavern some distance below, and at the far end of the cavern an old fire hearth, several feet deep in consolidated ashes, could be found with a little pulling away of fallen stone. The caverns were clearly shelters and communal homes in the bleak north European country of the time. In their own way they were cozy. Yet here and there leading from the far ends of the caverns narrow crevices no wider than a man could squeeze through continued more or less downward into the depths of the earth, fantastically lined with stalactite spikes and stalagmite curtains—eerie, unsafe, long and tortuous passages which you could too readily enter and not come back. And throughout Europe the cavernous systems are much the same—with secret and fearful labyrinths passing inwards, designed for secrecy and magic.

Certain cave drawings contain a heart placed properly within the outline of the animal and some show an arrow piercing its side, so that altogether the hoped-for prey is at times shown with the death-sending human hand, the death-bringing weapon and the death-receiving vital organ. Graphic symbolism, incantation and an acting-out of the hunting procedure in some ritual form all combined to make the hunters more likely to succeed in their business of providing the community with the meat necessary for its survival. Priest, sorcerer, medicine-man or whatever you prefer to call him, eventually took the place of the artist and became the transmittor of the condensed, ritualised knowledge and wisdom of the tribe. Sympathetic magic of this kind was far from being nonsense. It had, I am sure, the practical value of strengthening the will and confidence of the hunters preparatory to hazardous undertakings, with undertones and overtones of possibly hypnotic suggestion. It also contained the essence of prayer—the heartfelt death-wish, all the stronger for its unconscious sincerity, and just as surely, I think, the propitiary plea to the spirit of the intended victim. No dividing line was drawn between this nature and that, for animals were spirits who survived death in the same way as men, and killing was not lightly undertaken. Men knew that they had to kill in order to eat, but from everything we know of primitive hunting folk and from the internal evidence of the old cave pictures men also recognize the shattering impact of their own actions. Unspoken perhaps but unmistakably the ice age hunter said to the symbolic image of his prey 'God help me to kill you, but forgive me for doing so.' I have no doubt God was unformulated, but the divine is always the better for being undefined. Reverence for life is an ancient attitude and we should not need an Albert Schweitzer to recall it to us in our own day. Nor do I think that the placatory prayer to the spirit of the intended victim has been merely to safeguard the doer from the consequences of his deed. This may have been the conscious motive, but underneath has lain this recognition that when a man kills, whether the victim be an animal, a plant, or another man, no matter what the circumstances, there is an element of wrongness in the action. Is this the root of evil, so far back in time, yet not so far? For still farther back you cannot find it.

Magic is always a very practical affair, yet it involves a recognition of the supernatural, a belief in the power of magic, wielded by man, to turn aside the forces of the external world. Magic and religious ritual step in where knowledge fails and generally only when the action is beyond the normal capacity of man. He attempts to enact a miracle, not because he fails to recognise his own mental limitations but because he sees them. And if the primitive peoples of the present world are any sort of guide to the past, magic always consists of things said, things done, and an officiating individual. The fundamentals are the spell, the rite, and the condition of the performer, and they were probably as important in the cave of the antler-headed priest as they are now in Northwestern Australia or among the Indians of our own Southwest. The performer becomes hedged around with taboos; he must refrain from eating certain foods and from sexual indulgence, otherwise he nullifies his power; and he must assume an emotional state which overflows to his audience.

The spell itself however is the backbone of magic, the rigid setting of words fraught with ancient meaning and containing in obscure form some reference to great events in the history of the race, a secret bond with the past. The rite which accompanies the magical spell serves to convey the spell to the object which the group hopes to influence for better or for worse. All three function in a refined form to some extent in most of the older religions of mankind, our Christian Church by no means excepted. Yet in the more pagan past the spell, the rite and the master of ceremonies were more explicit, and we do not need to go back far to find them.

It is not much of a step from magic to black magic. They are the same thing seen in different lights, although how you see makes all the difference to the way you act. And in western civilization, quite apart from the burning contentions of Protestants and Catholics, the old pagan attitude to nature suffered horribly at the hands of the newer orthodoxy. Black magic evokes a picture of witchcraft, the devil and the dark of night. Yet witchcraft means the craft of the wise, devil is a word with the same root as divine and means little god, and the night has been for celebrating since time out of mind. The god is the old sorcerer come down through the ages but always in practice incarnate in a human being or an animal, for in the beginning the two were one as in the case of the cave-wall magician or many of the Egyptian gods. In medieval times the god, always addressed as the devil with no disrespect, appeared either in black to blend with the night or as an animal of a kind common in the region: a dog, cat or bull in England, a goat as well in France, and a jackal in prehistoric Egypt.

The assemblies or sabbaths took place four times a year and the dates show the year was divided at May and November, the most primitive of all man-made calendars. Old men, young men, women and children, hundreds of them, came to the feasts which lasted all night and ended at dawn. Fertility rites were practiced intensively with all the usual bars to promiscuity save those of incest broken down. The meetings were joyous and the practice of sympathetic magic which associated human propagation with that of animals coincided with the seasons of breeding in the animal kingdom. The rites had no relation to agricultural crops and have been supposed to refer to man's domesticated animals. I don't believe it. Animal domestication, apart from the dog who seems to have followed the hunter all over the world, now appears to have been a later enterprise than agriculture, and I am convinced that the fertility rites of the pagan religion of Europe, surviving in the witch cults almost to the present day, are directly descended from the practices of the reindeer mammoth people. They believed in the power of magic as ardently as any of their successors, for it was they who created it, and the fertility and the size of the populations of the animals they hunted, particularly as they grew to hunt perhaps too well, were of far greater urgency and import to them than to folk of later times who kept domesticated herds. The whole fertility religion with its peculiar association with time and place and practice holds the essence of the hunters, with all of their concern with the abundance or scarcity of game. From the earliest days, being obviously intelligent people of great awareness, they correlated the mating process with that of reproduction and projected it by magic rites to the wild animals they depended on but could not otherwise control. I have read that the human societies in Europe that succeeded the reindeer people and who introduced the beginnings of agriculture and certain domestic crafts came from east of the Mediterranean and that the ice age hunters themselves have not directly contributed to our western pedigree. It seems unlikely. The new people mixed with but did not displace the old, for else the hunters' religion would have died out too. Even in the end it did not die a natural death but was killed by the more forcible elements in the Christian Church, as definitely and as ruthlessly as the Spanish Catholics stamped out the religion of the Aztecs and the Incas. And it died a hard and grisly death as the power of the church spread northward in Europe during the 12th and 13th centuries, forcing the old religion into more and more secretive ways as Stone Age beliefs became the modern heresy, as the pagan devil became the personification of evil, as the lucky thirteen which was the religious unit of the witches became the unlucky number and the god in the form of a black cat became an evil omen; and the sound of cock crow, the old signal of the dawn and the end of the feast, became a sign of betrayal.

Yet alongside the fertility rites there survived the sacrifice, the ritual to encompass the death of the hunter's prey and perhaps to liberate its spirit, and in its most potent form it involved a human victim, finally as a form of appeasement of the mysterious unnameable power that controlled all outward events. The practice survived through the middle ages of Europe with ostensibly Christian leaders taking an active part, playing safe with regard to both the old god and the new. The witch's meetings, the covens, came to be a parody of the sacred rites of the church, themselves for the most part taken from pagan rites of another region, with the performance of the black mass as well as older magic. Witchery, enchantment, charm, fascination, glamor, entrancing, are all words from the world of witches and they ring the bells of poetry for us still. Human sacrifice however was the hardest to carry out, no matter how willingly the victim undertook the honor, and often enough the public executioner was duped to carry out the rite. The most notorious devil of witchcraft was Gilles de Rais, the Commander of Joan of Arc and Marshall of France, who was finally and justifiably condemned for sorcery after being convicted of sacrificing more than two hundred women and children in magic rites. Joan must have been fully aware of it all long before the battle of Orleans and a good case has been made that Joan herself was a voluntary Satanic martyr conveniently sacrificed by the English who merely considered it an execution. If so she is probably the only beatified witch in history.

Only in the twentieth century, and doubtfully even now in part of rural France and Italy, has the old cave man's religion completely disappeared, though our thoughts and speech are colored with it through and through. The collective human memory affects each and every one of us in ways we rarely are aware of, and it seems to me we are still the children of the hunters' moon.

14

POINTS OF VIEW

Culture, it is said, is a state of mind produced by the things you have forgotten. If so, then what you have forgotten or seem to have forgotten is as important in making you what you are as that which you remember. Taken together it is what binds a people into a cohesive whole and molds the lives and personalities of its component individuals. It is a human creation and is equally creative of much that is human, and one of the best definitions of man I have seen is that he is a culture-making animal. For he *is* an animal and encompasses everything that an animal is, and he also creates cultures, which no other animal does, and within his culture his soul develops. But not all cultures are the same.

Religion, art, the ethical codes by which a people live, the ways of doing things, all contribute to a particular culture and are expressions of it; all represent ways of thinking and the kinds of things that are thought about. Running through it all is language, not so much as the warp and woof of the woven fabric as the loom itself, directing the manner in which the cloth is made, yet built in the first place from the needs of men. Language is far more than a means for exchanging information and ideas or an outlet for pent-up emotions: it reveals and expresses a special way of looking at the world and interpreting experience. Every language conceals within its structure a vast array of unconscious assumptions about life and the universe, all that you take for granted and everything that seems to make common sense—the long forgotten history of thought itself, still coercing the living to think along the old established ways. Speech itself imprisons us, although in different ways, and each kind expresses a different view. What is sense to you may be nonsense to another, or the other way round. Each sees but a part, yet it is our supernal purpose to see the whole, and each human race needs to see through the eyes of another.

You cannot, for instance, get a straight 'yes or no' answer from a Chinese unless he is thinking and speaking in your language and not his own, for Chinese has no equivalents for such words or for their meanings, for Chinese thinking does not run to 'is it this or was it that' but to 'how is it or in what way.' Even when language is ostensibly the same, as in England and America, word values change and reveal differences in underlying attitudes: compromise in England is the admirable solution in which both sides gain as much as they should, compromise in America is an unsatisfactory and possibly cheapening outcome which pleases nobody. In Greek one and the same word may mean 'in the past' or 'in the future,' for the reason that the Greeks conceived themselves as living in a persistent present with time itself coming toward them and passing them by—they distinguished chiefly between 'now' and 'then,' and had no feeling of moving through time as we do. Yet the Greek, the Chinese and the Anglo-Saxon cultures are too vast to look at easily and in a short time, and to see a culture in relation to its language and people clearly we need to look for a smaller setting. And in the

Hopi Indians of the southwestern desert we find one sparkling like a jewel beneath the sun.

The ancient Hopi villages, perched high on their sun-drenched crags in northern Arizona may appear to be the last place on earth to look for enlightenment in a confused and warring world. Yet their isolation has been to a great extent their salvation and more than any other native group in the western hemisphere the Hopi have resisted the disintegrative pressures of coercive officials and proselytizing priests of an alien white civilization.

Hopiland still stands much as it did a thousand years ago, although the Hopi Indians have been in the grip of a serious and far-reaching crisis going back four centuries to the first contacts of the tribe with the Spaniards, a crisis aggravated by Navaho encroachment, by erosion, and by further exposure to a host of aggressive carriers of European culture and germs.

For over fifteen centuries at least the Hopi tribe has lived within a limited area under very rigorous circumstances. The arid northern plateau of Arizona has imposed conditions that have had to be coped with generation after generation for the tribe to survive, and in the face of intense and continuous environmental pressures the Hopi evolved a marvellously well adjusted social system.

An economy of scarcity has always prevailed and the very existence of the tribe has depended on the local and precarious water supply consisting of a few semi-permanent springs used for drinking water and garden irrigation, of moisture retained in sand dunes and used for dry farming, and periodic flood waters. And always there have been drought, sand storms, floods, frosts and pests to thwart human effort. Hunting has supplemented agriculture, but never to a very large extent in this region; while droughts have too often out-lasted the stores of food. Malnutrition, illness and premature death, particularly among children, has been the Hopi lot. Alto-

gether I doubt whether humanity anywhere has had to contend with harder times or found the problem of group survival more difficult to solve. Yet the Hopi have solved it and
in spite or perhaps because of hardships the group appears to
consist of the most fully developed and integrated individuals
existing anywhere on this planet. Full human stature is a
product of adversity, from the first to the last, and if the Hopi
are any criterion then serenity is gained by other means than
the pursuit of happiness. Yet the Hopi have had an ancient
past as well as a more recent one and it is this and the outlook
it imposes that concerns us at the moment.

You and I speak an Indo-European language that had its
original roots in the middle east somewhere around the Caspian Basin, from which it spread in various forms throughout
central and western Europe and across Asia Minor into India.
We all for instance use a recognisable variant of the word
'mother' derived from 'ma' meaning to make; and whether
we speak English or German, Celtic or Latin or Greek, or
Persian or some kind of Slavonik or Sanskrit, the basic point
of view implicit in the mother tongue is deeply ingrained in
the way we speak and think. The linguistic tools we have all
inherited determine the way we run our thoughts together,
how we distinguish between this or that phase of the world
around us, how we communicate what we see or what we
think to others, and to a great extent even how we behave
or act. No matter where you live or what the color of your
skin may be, if you speak a language of this family group you
are caught in its web, unaware of the strength of the gossamer
that binds you.

The Hopi and all other aboriginal peoples of the western
hemisphere are as remote from this particular persuasive fabric as it is possible to be, yet they have their own, within which
their thoughts are just as fully woven. Just who these Pueblo-
building Indians are is a matter for conjecture. We can trace

them back to the Basket-weavers of the same vicinity to about fifteen hundred years ago. Yet the southwestern plateau has been occupied by a people who lived on seeds and small game as long ago as 5000 B.C. Elsewhere on the continent men hunted bison and mammoth for thousands of years before that, and were even hunting or trapping the giant sloth at the southern tip of South America between eight and nine thousand years ago; the dates have been established by the new radioactive carbon techniques. Wherever they came from and whatever new strains may have reached and mingled with this ancient stock, there is little doubt of their great antiquity. Altogether I think there is every indication that the Hopi are the descendants of the early plateau people and that the basic habits of language and thought of the whole Aztec group to which they belong go back to this distant time and perhaps much farther. Both their outlook and their speech are in part the outcome of millenia spent on the high plateau country and in part an inheritance from an older way of life which seems to take root in the time when all men were hunters. Man in the Americas has had a long and complex history which has a fascination all its own, but in the present connection only a little of it is relevant and I wish simply to show that we may have to trace Hopi and Indo-European far into the chills of the ice age to find a common ancestral source. Any significant insight and elaboration of thought and expression we or the Hopi possess have become crystallized independently during our separate histories.

Provincialism is the curse of most human societies. The perspective of our own particular group is so ingrained within us that we feel no other can be good, that insofar as other human beings differ they are in error. When we come to a conclusion we follow it with a judgment and all too readily divide the world into black and white, sinners and saints, communist and Christian, or just plain stupid and wise. Com·

mon sense can be common and far from sensible and we cannot judge another's point of view until we have seen it. This
may be a platitude but it is also a truth we rarely accept fully,
not necessarily from unwillingness but simply from inability
to see or think except along the lines that our kind of language imposes upon us. Common sense is largely a matter of
talking so as to be understood by those who think more or less
in the same way. Space, time and matter seem to be common
sense concepts, relativity as many of us have somewhat woe-
fully discovered does not, in spite of all the supposedly helpful explanations offered to us. Yet Newtonian space, matter
and time are not common sense intuitions, they are out-
growths of our language and culture, where Newton found
them. Relativity is something else, an alien point of view so
far as most of us are concerned, which is why we cannot
readily grasp it.

The English language together with all the other Indo-
European and many other languages emphasize a kind of sentence having two parts, each part built round a class of word,
nouns and verbs, which grammar handles differently in the
various languages. The reason for it is simply that every language must have some sort of structure and this group happened to get started on this track. It is a distinction or contrast which we impose upon nature and is not something nature forces upon us. But Aristotle seized upon it and made it
a law of reason, and until a few centuries ago everything that
Aristotle said was gospel in the western world. This may not
seem very important, yet it has so affected our thinking that
it is difficult to exaggerate the consequences. We break everything down into things and relations between things, into
objects and their qualities, into actor and action, into planner
and plan. If we see order in the universe, then God must have
ordered it and those who fail to make the distinction must be
heathen or atheist.

The Hopi do not make this distinction. They have verbs without nouns, and would say 'flash' where we would feel compelled to say 'it flashed' or 'the light flashed.' When you think about it, 'flash' conveys all the quality of light, intensity and short duration, all of the action and the thing acting in one brief comprehensive whole. There are nouns too, but they are self-sustaining and a Hopi would say 'a water' where we have to encompass it in some way and say 'a pot of water' or 'a glass of water.' It is we who are awkward in our form of expression, making artificial distinctions where none is called for. And while Hopi will never be used for anything but Hopi talk, it is far more in keeping with our present concepts of the nature of the universe than the language we have grown up with.

The question of time itself looms very large, in the way I am talking, in the way I have been thinking, in the study of history, organisms, atoms and stars, and in our chronic concern over past, present and future. For a long time past I have felt trapped in time, like a prisoner searching desperately for some avenue of escape. It crops up in the way I write almost like an obsession, as witness the last two sentences. But the trap lies in the language and the manner in which it channels the course of my thought. Partly it comes from having learned to count but in this case doing so without proper distinctions. We say 'ten men' but we also say 'ten days.' The first you can see or remember having seen as an actuality—ten men can simultaneously exist as a group. But ten days you can only imagine—you have to conceive a day as a quantity of time and line up ten of them in a row. We have imposed a mental pattern upon our experience which is artificial, or else all languages would express it, and in doing so we have lost much of our real awareness of time—the sense of 'becoming later and later.' The Hopi have not lost it. Their language suggests nothing about time except the perpetual 'getting later' and they have no concept of 'time' as we conceive it.

Bear with me please for I am thinking aloud and feeling the weight of all the habits of thought my own language imposes on me. I find this effort to comprehend the Hopi outlook difficult, yet I am aware that our custom of thinking in the three tenses of present, past and future, which the Hopi lack, is in many ways a handicap to understanding and communicating, particularly when speaking of living processes. Biological time is notoriously different from cosmic or calendar time. Mouse time and man time have little reference to the circling of the earth around the sun, and you cannot judge a man's living age by his years. As a biologist I am acutely aware of the need for a new sort of language to describe the events that take place and constitute a living organism, just as physicists already use one incomprehensible to the rest of us. Yet our old 'common sense' approach does have its value. We objectify time something like an infinitely long ribbon marked off into equal blank spaces all calling for some kind of entry, which is exactly what I have been doing in this book. It is a treatment of time which is favorable to the keeping of records and history. It emphasises 'saving time' and puts a high value on speed. It coerces us into using calendars and clocks and all the commercial practices based upon them. We try to measure time more and more accurately, become conscious of the split second, produce efficiency experts, and hope to get from nowhere to nowhere in nothing flat. And still a minute can embrace eternity and a month be empty of meaning.

It comes as something of a shock to realise that a consistent picture of the immediate universe can be built up without such grand concepts as time, velocity and matter. Yet this is exactly what the Hopi have done, and while theirs is a limited view too it is very different from ours and is in its own way just as valid. Moreover it has been developed without the aid of any written language by a people until recently without technology except that of their own making. What is this view and what kind of lives and personalities are wrought up in it?

The Hopi thought-world has no imaginary space and so a Hopi cannot imagine a corn stalk, for instance, anywhere but where a corn stalk is. A Hopi thinking about a corn stalk naturally supposes that he himself, through his thought, is actually affecting the plant. His thought therefore must leave some trace of itself with the plant: if the thought is good, about health, it is good for the plant, or if the thought is bad, the plant suffers. This point of view finds no support in our own scientific outlook, which to a great extent is a captive of our thought and language patterns, but it has all the meaning of prayer and should not be scorned simply because our particular forms of common sense are all against it. And when thought has such power as this, intensity qualities become all-important, for effective or powerful thought must be vivid, clear, steady and sustained, and charged with good intention. Wrong thought has the power of evil. Consequently when any individual or group action is about to be undertaken, the Hopi enlist mental help from as many individuals as possible, partly to offset the harmful thought of ill-wishers but mainly to intensify the coercive power of purpose. Rooting for your side at a football game has something in common with it, although the Hopi get their hardest work done before the event and not during the action itself. One result is that in spite of the usual human bickerings the cooperative or community spirit of the Hopi village is outstanding in the present age of discord.

When you add to this practical belief in the power of thought the Hopi notion that time does not move but is a 'getting later' of all that has ever been done, power obviously may be stored up by repetition. So too the Hopi force is not motion or velocity as it is with us but is cumulation or acceleration, which are concepts of far greater content and far more in keeping with what we are now beginning to believe the nature of the universe to be, in spite of our 'common sense' bias. And in the Hopi language, which carries their thought, the modifiers of the seemingly concrete nouns are mainly of a large class of words denoting only intensity, tendency, duration and sequence, leading to abstractions almost beyond our power to follow. The greatest concern of the Hopi is the thought that prepares for rain and crops, upon which their lives depend, and the whole prolonged and intricate rituals and prayers of the rain ceremony is simply the natural expression of their belief in the power of desire and directed thought. We all are aware that we expend energy whenever we strongly desire or think intensively, and it is no more unnatural to consider thought as pervading the universe than to believe that light does. In fact without something comparable to this the universe as conceived by science makes no sense to me. This is a theme however which leads too far afield for the present.

The whole world of man can be measured against a Hopi town. It is not only that it is small enough for the community to be more or less face to face but that the group is a democratic unit not unlike the ancient Greek city state, independent and sufficient unto itself. Public opinion is powerful and inescapable, leaders and people are closely associated, decisions are usually made by unanimous consent, and every individual is responsible for the welfare of the whole. Privilege does not exist, all thought and culture are directed toward the ideal of peace; religious tradition functions as the constitution; and all Hopi institutions express faith in a harmonious universe in which nature, man and all living things are mutually interdependent, bound together for the benefit of all. Leadership is unsought and is burdened with heavy moral responsibility. All in all the community is like the crew of a ship in a storm, bound together by the goal of survival, with every soul in its place. The analogy is close, for as in the ship any betrayal of the common purpose may be disastrous when there is no margin for error, which has been the Hopi lot. And against this we see the wider world of man as a compounded confusion of purpose, uncertainty of method, and multiplicity of voice, desperately in need of direction and harmony.

Whether the organization of Hopi society within the community can be regarded as a model or not is beside the point. Our need is to see ourselves more clearly than we do and until we make a definite comparison we are not likely to know how we look or what ails us. Yet the intrinsic interest of Hopi custom is great and I have a strong feeling that we should take good note of it while it is still possible to see it in anything like its original purity. For in the long run the Hopi as such have about as much chance of survival under modern pressures as the Whooping Cranes and Trumpeter Swans. To be outstandingly different, particularly if beautiful and defenseless, is to invite destruction in these days of advanced and intolerant civilizations, and the Hopi have been as much under fire as any other rare and colorful creation.

Hopi institutions consist of clans and societies superimposed upon and pervading the family units, closely bound up with tribal religion and the world view. Each clan is a true blood-grouping consisting of one or more lines descending from a single female ancestor, at least in theory. The heart of the clan is a group of related females consisting of an elderly active woman who is the real head, her sisters, and all their descendants. Her brothers and all the male descendants, but not relatives by marriage, belong to the same clan. A

Hopi considers himself a member of three maternal lines—his mother's, his father's and his mother's father's—into none of which can he marry. Close inbreeding is thus prevented and racial health is maintained. The clan collectively owns the springs, gardens and farm lands. The house, all stores of food and furnishings, and also the children, belong to the group of women within the clan; and in each household the women and girls care for the children, grind corn, garden, and make pottery and baskets. The Hopi women thus own practically all property of any value except livestock and a Hopi woman has social and economic security independent of her marital status. The female grows up within a system that gives priority to her sex in ways that recognize her special responsibilities, namely the breeding of good human stock and control of the means of life. Whether this goes back to an ancient wisdom acquired in the old world or whether it is an independent example of the innate good sense of humans which has evolved in the new I do not know. Its origin matters less than the wisdom it expresses, for in such a system the goal is health and life, with no room for thoughts of war and death. I have a feeling however that we see here expressed in actual practice much of the old accumulated understanding of human values that early man acquired over a long period of time, retained by the Hopi in almost unsullied form but over-ridden elsewhere by intrusive forces.

If this were all, then the recognition of the female as the biologically more significant sex, and the fundamental female-centered kinship system which is the natural and practical outcome of this recognition, would place women in the dominant position. But the male has a compensatory activity. Apart from their common business of farming, herding, hunting, and collecting fuel, the products of which they contribute to the households of their mothers, fathers and father's sisters, much of their time is spent in ceremonial action and preparation.

Just as the female is placed upon the biological throne, so the male, who is always more of a problem, tends to weave a spell that gives him eminence. The head of a clan is a woman, but the ceremonial head is her brother who works not with the clan but with other members of a secret religious society drawn from the community as a whole. The male societies control the major religious ceremonies and are secret associations open to voluntary membership by those willing to accept the responsibilities. They control all the complicated ritual connected with communal welfare and their outlook on nature as a whole, and the leaders of the societies form a council with disciplinary authority and the capacity to lead in any state of emergency. The male in other words is given pre-eminence in his masculine ability for true leadership and in his imaginative performance with symbolic magic. Each sex has its place in a well balanced society. Children grow under the benevolent guidance of numerous uncles and aunts as well as their own parents and sisters. Personalities are nourished to full maturity. Combined with it all is the constant emphasis on the power of concentrated thought and the ever present threat of economic disaster. The personalities which develop are quietly poised, serenely content, inwardly intense, and intellectually adept at problem-solving—fully formed human spirits capable of great concentration and mental effort. Each individual funtions independently and cooperatively within the society, directed from within and not by outside coercions. It is not surprising I think that all intelligence tests of Hopi children rank them, in contrast to most white children and all other Indian tribes, as on the average very intelligent, highly observant, and capable of complex, abstract thinking.

If we conveniently forget the official treatment of Indian groups in the past, the greatest threat to the survival of this

isolated forcing house of human personalities is the evan-
gelical missionary, in this case the Mennonite, in his most
uncompromising and destructive form. The missions teach
above all the doctrine of original sin and the threat of deferred
punishment, of subordination of the spirit and mind of man to
an unwarranted feeling of guilt, aggravated here by disapproval
or forbiddance of responsible leadership within Hopi society.
Anxiety, personality disturbance, and a tendency to social
disruption, so familiar outside the Hopi world, make their
appearance to the extent the missions are successful. The
selfrighteous, who regard heresy as sinful, sin more than
their victims.

In many ways the Hopi appear to represent human society
in general as it seems to have been during the new stone age
which began shortly after the end of the last glacial period.
Their only animals, before white man arrived to add his own
collection, were the dog who is a spiritual companion from
hunting days, and the turkey. Yet they show the human
mind at its best—at peace with itself, coping with existence,
and regarding the world as a balanced but complex system
governed by an inner rhythm which includes all men, animals,
plants, the sun and the moon, clouds and rain, spirits and
ancestors, as parts of a single harmonious whole.

15

THE FACE OF CIRCUMSTANCE

We are a restless race and seem to enjoy a certain amount of discomfort. The perfect unchanging climate soon becomes monotonous and a blustering storm a welcome sight. We look for change and no matter how much we may complain we seem to like the unpredictable swing from wet to dry or warm to cold. Our language itself, as well as our conversation, reflects obsession with the weather, as though it were the most potent external force that we have to cope with.

A climate may be invigorating or enervating, depending somewhat on who you are, while incessant change itself is stimulating, calling for continual mental and physiological adjustment which keeps mind and body keyed to a high pitch. Seasons, changing climates and everyday weather seem to reach into our bones and mold both our actions and our thoughts. We pray for rain, like the Hopi, when there is too little of it and not so long ago we all prayed to our gods to remove the curse when we suffered from floods; now when Europe is miserable from too much winter rain and storms the cause is assigned to hydrogen bomb explosions, as though climatic changes were unknown and unthinkable and only man's own sins of commission or omission could be held responsible. Yet there is little so fickle as atmospheric circulation and the precipitation which it causes, and for several decades at least the pine and spruce forests of the world have been creeping slowly north across the Arctic tundra, while farther south the birch dies from too much warmth. Glaciers melt and the day may be nearer than we think when the arctic ice pack thins and suddenly melts.

Rapid and frequent climatic change has been the common experience of mankind throughout the last million years. Had there been no ice caps with their violent fluctuations and the seasons they have evoked, I am sure that neither you nor I nor any other human would be here to speak of them. A somewhat different ape-like stock might have given rise to something like us at another time, but under such different circumstances it is hard to say what might have appeared. As the climate has changed, so have we, and as climatic zones have shifted so men have moved accordingly, and never for long have human beings been left in peace. We are the products of tropical heat and glacial cold, and even now we do not know whether we are really pulling out of the ice age or are just somewhere in the interval between the fourth and fifth glacial advance. We live on a lively planet and underestimate its capacity to shape our destiny.

Cave-haunting men backed with the knowledge and warmth of fire and armed with throwing-spears pushed north to the edge of the glaciers and prevailed against the cold during the last advance of the ice sheets; their world was bleak, forbidding and beautiful, with dry summers and savage winters. Yet game was abundant and mammoths, bison, reindeer, musk oxen, horses and other animals browsed on the grassy steppes and tundra of central Europe and elsewhere; salmon ran every year in the rivers of central France as abundantly as they do today in the Columbia and Frazer rivers of North America. The times were prosperous in terms of food and energy. The hunters enjoyed their hunting and the human communities were well fitted to the life they led. From the peak of the last ice phase, about 35,000 years ago, until about 10,000 B.C. the well made, large-brained hunters dwelt in strong communities throughout western and eastern Europe, never in doubt that the great beasts and the open lands would last forever. They killed their accustomed prey with flint-headed spears, used flint chisels not only for their art but for carving bone and ivory, made needles with which the women sewed warm skins into efficient garments, and toward the end of their time made harpoons with which they harpooned seals and, somewhat later, whales. Yet finally the ice sheets melted and the great age of the hunters came to an end.

As the glaciers melted and the ice retreated northward, the rain belt shifted from the grassy plains of Arabia and the Sahara across the Mediterranean to southern Europe, and as it moved, life shifted too.

A climatic wave of this intensity is awesome when seen in retrospect with time foreshortened, although year by year or even from one generation of men to the next the change may have been too small to have been disturbing—perhaps no more than we are now experiencing. Yet over a period of one or two thousand years, may be somewhat more, possibly less, much of northern Africa and Arabia changed from the World's garden to the burning deserts familiar to us, while forests crept north across the steppes and the tundra of Europe, forcing the reindeer ever closer to the northern rim of the continent and reducing bison to a fraction of their old numbers. Mammoths had already followed the fate of the woolly rhinoceros, possibly from overhunting but probably mainly from inability to cope with the everincreasing quagmires and flood waters, victims of their own enormous weight. In any case the upshot was much the same: the hunting societies of greater Europe dwindled and degenerated as dense woodlands took the place of the wind-swept game-filled landscapes, and they survived only to the extent that they could adjust to the new conditions. That many did survive I think is shown by the character of the witchcult rites of pagan Europe.

It is a poor wind however that fails to fill a vacuum. As cool rain raised the forests and strangled the civilization of the hunters in central and western Europe, warmer rains along the Mediterranean shores brought rich tropical vegetation to the coastal belt of Spain, and a new society of men appeared who apparently came from Africa across the Strait of Gibraltar. They also were rock painters, with a style of their own, and their drawings clearly show the new shape of circumstance. They drew on a smaller scale, drew scenes rather than individual animals, and drew in the sunshine and not in the deep and dark recesses of caves. In a general way the drawings resemble those of South Africa made by bushmen and other negroid races, but the self portraits made by the people of Spain are those of full-sized men and women with thick shoulder-length hair.

The paintings reflect both the people and the world they lived in. Big game animals are missing, though wild boar and deer in the forests and ibex in the hills were reason enough for hunting. The large birds of earlier times, the eagle, goose and raven, are still shown, but so are flamingo, spoonbills, storks and glossy ibis, all of them magnificent, warmth-loving wading birds indicating a warm wet climate. So also does the drawing of two women climbing a long 60 foot rope-like liana vine to get at a wild bees' nest, the whole suggesting honey and flowers and great trees with pendent vines typical at present only of tropical forests. When the ice finally went, the end may have been sudden and greater warmth than we now know bathed the middle latitudes. A feeling almost of gaiety is expressed in these sketches in Southern Spain and the hunters are portrayed more vigorously and abundantly than the animals they hunted, always running with a tremendous leap or stride, or kneeling with bows flexed and arrows sailing through the air. And where shown at all, clothing consisted of breeches alone, possibly as protection against thick underbrush but leaving the body free to sweat in the humid heat. The bow is seen here for the first time and may have been their own invention or may have been brought over from Africa where fleeter animals than the reindeer of the north demanded a more effective weapon than a throwing-spear.

How the bow was even invented has troubled me a lot, for while it is the first power machine ever made and is obvious enough once you have seen it, the concept itself is just one of those deceptively and monumentally simple things that even the greatest genius can hardly dream up out of nothing. Step by step the idea of the bow has led to the thought of sending rockets to the moon, but not even the jet-propelled rocket has the fresh clarity of original creation that the bow possesses. The motive behind the bow, the whole business of guided missiles, I am not here concerned with. Great needs do not necessarily give rise to great inventions, whether mechanical or sociological, for minds work in their own peculiar way, although human needs ring the bells when answers are reached. The problem that has fascinated me is how a human mind first conceived a bow with its taught string, bent wood, and power to send a light spear far faster and farther than a man can throw. In fact I do not believe that any such creation sprang fully formed from any mind, for it demands a quality of thought and mental projection far beyond my own. This may call for an obvious retort, but we do not conceive as possible anything we cannot truly imagine, and in this respect at least I am typical.

Human inventiveness comes from observation, discovery, attentiveness, and the conscious or subconscious brooding that follows later when impressions are no longer pouring in through the senses. And the bow I think grew out of a putting together of simple discoveries idly made or perhaps from watching children at play, for ideas come to the surface when pressures are most relaxed; in our present age of turmoil the bathtub is notoriously more conducive to inspiration than an office or a laboratory, let alone driving through city traffic. The principle of the bow was known, I feel sure, before ever a bow was made, and I think it came from tropical nature combined with the playful activities of boys. It may be no coincidence that these later Spanish rock drawings show tropical lianas stretching from tree branch to the ground and also show the bow in action. For in Africa even now youngsters use the slender vines taughtly stretched between earth and branch as a bow string, pulling back with a crotched stick and letting it go to fly like an arrow. Of no value except as a game it gives the mind the essential fact of the power of a spring. It is not too great a step from the ready-made bow of nature to the manufactured one, but so far as I can see only the tropical vines, the natural curiosity of boys with time on their hands, and the driving need of the hunter to improve the range and efficiency of his guided missiles, could in combination have produced the bow. And from this beginning all our machines for accumulating energy for subsequent sudden release for good or evil have come into being. Quite apart from the principle itself, perhaps the most potent mechanical concept in human history, the bow eventually became the cross-bow, then the musket, cannon, and at last the rockets and the air-borne bombs. Yet it started probably in warm rain forests in Africa some ten thousand years ago as the result of children's games. So much of our trouble, from first to last, has arisen from innocent playfulness, either actual or mental. The devil finds mischief for idle hands to do has a peculiarly human intonation.

The history of man seems inextricably bound up with the history of trees and the rain that sustains them both. Tropical forests made the most of us, the absence of trees gave us our chance to run and made us into hunters, and temperate woodlands changed us into agriculturists and industrialists. At each stage we have adjusted to circumstances. Now we seem to be conquering our environment, which may be a deadly thing to do. Yet for the last ten thousand years we have felt the winds of climatic change for better and for worse. Harkening backward into the dimness of the preglacial past we hear only the faint sounds of sub-human stirrings. Through the near million years of the surging ice age as a whole the sound of the human march is more definitely heard, but we hear it as the sound of singing many turns away down the road. When the ice melted for the fourth time it is as though the human band turned the final corner and the full blast of voices suddenly roars down to us through the time remaining. These are our own people at last, moving at an ever-increasing pace if we measure pace by the rate of change.

If modern type man has existed at least from the great interglacial period, with several hundred thousand years elapsing until the present, with all their vicissitudes of ice and water, why did so little human change occur up to the time of the last melting? Were the conditions during the period of the great floods which accompanied the melting of the ice caps so different on this last occasion from the one before, or was it mankind that was different? Shakespeare wrote that there is a tide in the affairs of men which, taken at the flood, leads on to fortune. All we know is that on the fourth and last time when the icy flood gates were opened man was ready for his great adventure. And it may have been little things that turned the tide.

A man's view of the world and of life depends on his vantage point. The hunter's paradise of open plains and plateaus was shattered as forests grew where no trees had been, and a new people spread through the lands from regions somewhere around the Caspian Sea in Western Asia. They were as much at home in the woodlands as the hunters were oppressed by them, and their contribution to the conquest of the earth was the polished stone ax. The ax was not flaked like the old hand axes but was hard stone ground to a fine cutting edge and mounted in a wooden shaft. It was the first ax that a man could use to cut down trees large enough for building a house, making sleds or canoes, or hewing planks. The oldest axes so far found are those of the Caspian region and are of a period about 6000 B.C. In all probability the ax spread much faster than the people who had made it, and I have little doubt that the descendents of the reindeer and mammoth hunters were as quick to recognise and adopt a good thing when they saw one as any other variety of humans, just as in New Guinea during the last twenty years virtually all the native tribes have given up making polished stone axes in favor of importing steel axes from Europe and North America. The bow gave rise to the gun and we are in a fair way to clearing the earth of all non-human competitors. The ax has remained the ax in spite of the switch from stone to metal, and over most of the earth we are still cutting down the forests faster than they can grow. Taken together in fact the bow and polished ax may yet turn out to have been the heralds of a planetary bleakness I hate to contemplate.

Possibly the most significant and fascinating but least known regions of the earth is that heart of the world continent known as the Caspian basin—least known inasmuch as it seems to be a somewhat mysterious no-man's-land inaccessible from more directions at once than almost any other, and ignored to a greater extent than most. Yet more has gone on in this region to affect the fate of mankind than anywhere else, with the changing climate primarily calling the tune. Here is the hub of the human earth, with land routes open to Europe, Africa, India and northeast Asia, the center from which disturbances spread with devastating effect like a pot boiling over.

We need first I think to look at the whole of humanity, so far as we know it, during that pregnant period known as the mesolithic, that deceptively quiescent interval between the Old Stone age that ended with the replacement of ice and tundra by forests and the New Stone age that came into being with the drying out of the land and that in many ways is with us yet.

The neanderthal types of men had long since disappeared. The Old Stone age hunters, never very abundant, had spread to the ends of the earth, through Europe and Asia to Australia, Japan, and the Americas—people, not too unlike the present European stock, if we judge by the remnants surviving as the aborigines of Australia, the hairy Ainus of Japan and the handful of Tierra del Fuegians. A mongoloid race came into being somewhere in northeast Asia during the late phase of the ice, ready to spread south in China and east across the Bering Strait in the wake of the earlier men. While negroid pygmy bushmen occupied the great arc of moist tropical forest from central Africa through India and southeast Asia into the Indonesian islands and as far south as Tasmania; dwarfed forest people of great antiquity.

This oversimplifies the picture to be sure but generally speaking I think it serves our purpose.

Why the bushmen should be dwarfed I am not certain. A small slender body may be much better suited to the humid heat of the rain forests than one of full stature, both for keeping cool and for proficiency in forest hunting. Yet bushmen are not the only pygmies in the forest and the continual leaching of essential mineral salts from the soil by the heavy rains may well have favored the survival of small types of men and other animals, whose individual mineral needs for bone growth are less demanding. In any case life has grown on the rich and humid forests lying south of the equator more or less unchanged from sometime in the late ice age until the present and the main events stem from the northern hemisphere.

If we forget the shrinkage of the south polar ice cap as being entirely outside our field of action, and the melting of the glaciers of North America as affecting only a secondary theater of human affairs, the great melting that set mankind upon its present course came from three glacial centers of Scandinavia, the Alps, and to some extent at least, the high ranges of the northwest Himalayas. Ice and snow covering the higher lands lying within the great amphitheater so marked undoubtedly added much to the watery confusion. At this time the Caspian Sea was joined to the Black Sea, but the narrow outlet to the Meriterranean through the Bosphorus had yet to be found. The combined inland sea, which was a relic of an even larger inland sea of more ancient times, once washed the border of Afghanistan to the south but flowed northward toward the Arctic ocean along the line of the Volga river. At present the Volga and other rivers drain into a Caspian Sea of reduced size, though still the better part of a thousand miles long, in which seals and herring and sturgeon still abound, living evidence of the old connection with the ocean. The present size of the Caspian is a balance struck between the inflow of water from the rivers and evaporation from the surface, and the saltiness of the desert steppes to the east indicates its former extent. Yet along the southern and western borders of the sea bounded by the Persian plateau and also to the north the land is entirely different, as rich as the other is poor. Such is the stage, the cradle of the bulk of the human race in the usual historical sense, and across it lay the great caravan camel route to China, the road from Istanbul to Samarkand, the road to India over the Hindu Kush, the road to Europe through the Danubian corridor, and by way of the plateau to Mesopotamia, Egypt, and points west.

I find it difficult to imagine the wateriness that soaked the temperate lands during the centuries the ice cap was melting fast. Between them the reed-filled swamps and lagoons and the tree-covered hills changed the face of the land; while the tremendous run-offs carried enormous quantities of rich soil down the mountain slopes to form fertile deltas at the mouth of rivers. Clearly if man was ready for a new adventure, the time was ripe. And for the first time we can assign definite dates since the period falls well within the effective range of the radioactive carbon dating technique.

A few dates from the western hemisphere are useful for comparison. Trees smashed by advancing glaciers in Wisconsin when the ice sheet was last at its farthest south date somewhere between 9000 and 10,000 B.C. Woven rope sandals recovered from a cave in Oregon date at about 7000 B.C. While burned bones of horse and giant sloth associated with human bones and articles found in a cave at the southern tip of Chile date around 6500 B.C.

In Europe, charcoal from a cave in central France which contains paintings of the reindeer people dates at about 9000 B.C. The paintings of course may be older, but this is approximately the time of the far southern advance of the ice sheet in North America, and such evidence as we have indicates that the climatic events in the two hemispheres were synchronized. Yet the charcoal came from a human occupation level associated with two kinds of conifers neither of which grow in a cold climate. Apparently the climate was already mild some time before the ice itself significantly changed to melted water.

The immediate and general effect of the new swamps and forests was the obvious one. Travel was impeded and human communities were forced to become more sedentary. The big game hunters felt the severest restriction and had to make the most adjustment. How well or badly they succeeded is hard to say; but people already inclined by force of circumstance to hunt lesser game and fish, and by virtue of a more luxuriant environment able to gather fruit and seeds in quantity, clearly had a natural advantage. Excavations at Belt Cave in northern Iran, lying between the southern shore of the Caspian Sea and the steep slopes of the Elburz Mountains, show the general sequence of the great transformation. The lowest level excavated yielded many seal bones, some of them burned, which date at about 8600 B.C., together with evidence of a wet climate. The ice age was over and the rains and floods had arrived. Somewhat later, perhaps by a thousand years, mesolithic people still occupied the area, but the climate was apparently drier and the gazelle replaced the seal as the primary source of meat. Then came a level in which the bones are those of domesticated sheep and goats, domestication being indicated by the fact that a high proportion of the bones are those of lambs and kids; and later again, at about 6000 B.C., there are not only sheep and goats but pigs as well, together with primitive pottery and sickles for reaping grain. The New Stone age revolution had been accomplished, and nowhere else in the world has an earlier dating for it been found.

Saying it like this suggests that the neolithic revolution happened quickly. So much depends on what yardstick we use for time. Looking backward from the present, then the period involved is of the same order as the whole of the Christian era, but looking at it from the interminable length of the Old Stone age of the hunters one or two thousand years is brief indeed. In terms of rate of change, the pace quickens greatly. Moreover, in terms of more significant time, probably no more than fifty human generations and possibly less were responsible for the greatest transformatior and the greatest inventions in the whole of human history. Following any trail is a relatively easy matter but doing something that no one has ever thought of doing before is not only difficult, it is nearly impossible. Just as new ideas dawn slowly for an individual, so I am sure that in the case of a collective change of such magnitude the clarity of understanding we seem to see from here is an illusion gained from hindsight and the whole process of thought and action responsible for the cultivation and breeding of plants and animals which took the place of the old gathering and hunting was in reality a prolonged and heart-breaking effort of the human mind. Only now I think do we begin to appreciate in the light of present day biological science how much insight and ingenuity went into the creation of agriculture and animal husbandry by a people who lived some eight to nine thousand years ago. And only a people more or less anchored to fertile and well watered lands for an unlimited time could have had much chance to so transform the whole manner of human existence. The southern shores of the Caspian still offer all the requisite opportunities and probably did so on an even more extended scale during the time in question. The climate is mild, the rainfall heavy and the soil rich and black. The rivers are still full of sturgeon. Wild fruit of many kinds we now enjoy in cultivated form are abundant—peaches, pears, plums, almonds, apricots, apples and grape; while pheasants, grouse, ducks and geese abound in the swamps and among the hills; higher up among the mountain forests wild sheep, boar, goats and deer are still plentiful, and at one time so were wild cattle. The opportunity existed and the evidence indicates that the right men were in the right place at the right time to make the shift that led the way to the modern world.

There is more however than a few excavations within a natural garden of Eden to point to this region of the earth as the original nursery of the new life. The animals and plants that have been domesticated tell an even more conclusive story. There are or have been many forms of wild sheep, goats, pigs and oxen and the question has been which of them have been the ancestors of the domesticated forms. The argument is not entirely over but the most favored candidate for the domesticated goat is one that lives wild in Turkestan and Afghanistan, while the sheep is a kind found in the mountains south of the Caspian Sea. The pig in its earlier western form undoubtedly came from the wild boar that ranges from Africa and Europe to Siberia although in more recent times we have substituted the short-faced kind that belonged to southeast Asia. Cattle are a little more difficult, for the ox is thought to be a descendent of the huge, hot-tempered longhorn pictured in the hunters' caves, in the Minoan murals of ancient Crete, and whose sacrifice is still commemorated in the ceremonial bull fights of Spain. After Europe became forested it became restricted to the plains of Southern Russia and the Caspian Basin. Yet the first domesticated ox was a dwarf. Either the neolithic men bred a small race from the great unmanageable beast of the plains or they found and took advantage of a dwarf race that lived in the forests. The last seems to be the case, for where man has taken a wild animal and subsequently dwarfed it, as in the bulldog, the teeth remain too large for the jaws, whereas in natural dwarfs everything is in proportion.

Cereals, the first and foremost of domesticated plants, were originally wild mountain grasses. Two wild grasses ancestral to wheat are known, dinkel and wild emmer, the first growing throughout the whole of the Caspian and Black Sea region, the second farther south in Palestine and parts of Persia. Dinkel is the parent of a small unsatisfying wheat widely grown in Europe in prehistoric times and still cultivated in Asia Minor, while emmer seems to have been the oldest kind grown in Egypt, Asia Minor and western Europe. Most modern bread wheats however appear to be a cross between emmer and an unknown grass and it is this hybrid which is the oldest type found in Persia, Turkestan, Mesopotamia and India. Barley ancestors also appear to have belonged to the general region of mountainous country around the Caspian Basin. Cereal grasses undoubtedly were gathered head by head before they were cultivated and no tool is needed for the purpose, but cultivation combined two remarkable discoveries or inventions. Strains of wheat, barley and rye were discovered that grew heads which did not shatter and scatter their grain, a suicidal type for a wild grass to be but ideal for the human cultivator who could bide his time and reap his crop all at once. And flint sickles were made for cutting the hard stemmed grasses. Neither non-shattering cereals nor the sickles they inspired were acquired in a hurry.

All of this was only the beginning, but it was enough to give the neolithic people a positive control over their supplies of food and energy. It also gave them, in the form of captive meat on the hoof and grain that could be stored as food and seed, freedom to travel without wondering where the next meal would come from. And travel they did.

16

RAIN, RACE AND TRANSITION

GIVEN additional food and security any organism takes a new lease on life, and man has been no exception. As breeders of a number of domesticated animals to serve for meat, milk and clothing, and as cultivators of grains that could be sown, harvested or stored as occasion demanded, neolithic men were assured of an increased and fairly steady supply of food. And as long as the human population was small in relation to the land it was beginning to farm there was no need for any sort of permanent settlements—as crops exhausted the soil or herds tended to overgraze, all that was necessary was to move on to more virgin territory and plant anew. Such seems to have been the custom at first along the shores of the Caspian, with caves used as shelters as from time immemorial. Sooner or later however under the circumstances of nature's benevolence and human ingenuity the primitive farming communities were bound to grow and spread over adjacent lands. Population pressure made itself felt and as human numbers rocketed under the new conditions the people on the fringe moved further and further from the centers of neolithic life, as though a human spring slowly bubbled up in the Caspian lands and ripple after ripple spread out in all directions, except perhaps to the north and the northeast.

Caves however have always been in short supply and since in the course of the long ages some instinct for a home of a sort seems to have become firmly ingrained in the human fibre, externalized caves in the form of huts made with mud and wattle or with slight timber framing filled in with reed mats took care of the sensitive souls and bodies when night or winter wind oppressed them. Clusters of such huts formed the first villages in history, and in the course of time as the debris of human occupation and successive replacements of shelters accumulated, mounds or kells rose like pimples on the land near rivers and the shores of lakes. They are a common sight along the margins of the Caspian Sea and the more favorable parts of Turkestan and elsewhere in western Asia.

Yet the rain belt which lay across the desert latitudes of Africa and Arabia during the glacial phase did not leap northward to its present zone all at once when the ice melted. For a time, possibly for two or three thousand years altogether, while it moved imperceptibly north, the most favored zone was the Mediterranean and its eastward climatic extension along the line of the Black Sea and Caspian Sea to the central Asian plateau. Great forests of oak covered the northern edge of Africa even while the Sahara grasslands were shrinking to oases centered about the damper places, and for the same reason rich forests covered the hills and valleys of Asia Minor. Between the latitudes of 30 and 45 degrees north on the map of Europe and western Asia you will see the lands most benefited. They comprise the so-called cradle of civilization, that of China excepted. What the course of human history would have been if the rain belt had remained within these intermediate latitudes is impossible to say. It would have been greatly different I am sure, probably much less bloody, less neurotic and atomic. There's little point in guessing, although it is always fun to figure what might have happened had conditions remained unchanged or taken a different course from the one they have.

Human history in the modern sense begins with this setting of small neolithic villages in a Mediterranean belt of western Asia seven to eight thousand years ago, and it has continued up to the present under the erratic pressures of expanding population and continually changing climate. The present is a climax when population waves have reached the rim of the world and are rolling back upon themselves, where adverse climate is to be coped with rather than escaped from, and where there is no longer any place to go. It is a natural point in time from which to look at the whole sweeping event of which there is continuous record.

It is difficult to see much of this event in anything like its totality, not only because we are so close to it that we find it hard to see the wood for the trees but because the reality is something which has gone on in so many dimensions at once that the mind rebels in trying to grasp it. The marvel, I suppose, in view of our more remote ancestry, is that we can comprehend as much as we do. Yet the imagination we have so far acquired has its limits and sooner or later we each of us find ourself frustrated. I am able to contemplate only one aspect of this history at a time, which I find difficult enough.

We are concerned here with a human society growing through space, time and culture. As the population grew it spread outward from the periphery, like a thin film spreading from a denser center, the marginal people forever being driven by population pressure behind them to venture farther and farther into unknown lands. But as the fringe moved slowly into distant regions the more stable and flourishing people of the heartland progressively developed their culture. Society at home carried the arts and craft of village life to higher levels while the small colonies or tribes penetrating the rim of their little world carried with them only the culture they possessed at the time of their earlier departure. So it is we find primitive pottery and sickles for reaping grain in the cave on the southern Caspian land as early as about 6000 B.C., but on the far southern side of the Persian plateau, in northern Mesopotamia, a village mound that has been dated by the same radioactive carbon method as a little younger than 5000 B.C. shows that the people made no pottery, although they cultivated cereals and bred sheep, goats, pigs, and cattle. They either migrated across the plateau before pottery making had begun or they lost the art in transit. But at Jericho, another six hundred miles to the southwest across the Syrian desert, the bottom-most layer of a mound, which also dates at about 5000 B.C., also represents people who were ignorant of pottery manufacture, although they left us skulls with faces of plaster expertly molded to the likeness of the living and of a type of face common in many parts of Europe even now. So that the picture we get is of small bands pushing ever farther into the wilderness, settling down wherever conditions permit, and carrying with them such practices and skills as they had when the migrations first began. And in 5000 B.C., or thereabouts, the outlying groups were already something like a thousand years behind the times, at least so far as making pottery was concerned. Yet woe betide the early adventurers who were overtaken by a later wave of migrants coming over the mountains equipped with the superior weapons and fighting techniques which had been developed in the meantime.

The vanguards however continued to push along the paths of least resistance. During these early millenia of our era north Africa was still fairly well watered and was yet to feel the full impact of man with his ax and his animals. Forests of oak extended along most of Africa bordering the Mediterranean and at about 3000 B.C., possibly five or six hundred years earlier, neolithic people arrived at the strait of Gibraltar, having followed their pigs almost acorn by acorn for the better part of two thousand miles, but taking close on two thousand years to make the journey. Some of them managed to cross the strait to continue the slow infiltration through Spain to settle in France and the British Isles, while another spearhead moving out of Asia Minor settled in Greece, Crete and Italy. Others again took a northwesterly course around the Caspian Sea and Black Sea to follow the banks of the Danube, finally to reach Germany and mingle with the migrant wave that had come from North Africa through Spain. Both branches carried with them the technique for making soft pottery and for making black stone axes. Improved techniques also traveled the paths of migration as later folk continued to emigrate, but at about the same pace so that painted pottery for instance reached Germany by traffic along the Danubian corridor about a thousand years after it had originated in the Caspian homeland.

The slow fanning out to the west took in Mesopotamia, Egypt, both shores of the Mediterranean and its eastern islands, and most of Europe. The same steady pressure of people from the Caspian basin took them into the highlands of Afghanistan, through the Kyber Pass and down into the Indus Valley, and took others across Turkestan to the Upper Yellow River Valley leading to China, and eventually through Korea to Japan. All along these routes traces of the slender-boned white Caucasian race still exist, in its blond or in its darker form. The drive of the Mongols from northeast Asia through China and Indochina as far as the Ganges Valley of India is another story, although they caught the neolithic cultivator infection as it drifted eastward and developed it in their own good way in southeast Asia. The more distant parts thus colonized, such as China, may not have been reached much before 2500 B.C.

Man proposes, but God disposes. The hoe-cultivators who farmed the northern slopes of the Persian plateau and husbanded domesticated cloven-hooved animals evolved their art at a time when the climate was getting warmer and drier. Rain fell on the hills but judging from present conditions probably little fell on the lowlands north of the mountains. No matter how much nomadic garden culture was practiced, grain most likely was sown in the rich black mud along the banks of the rivers where they crossed the plain, periodically irrigated by the natural flow of water. It would have taken but little ingenuity to give nature a boost by digging shallow irrigation channels with the black stone hoes used for cultivating. There is in fact very little doubt that irrigation farming was developed almost from the beginning and that it was part of the cultural techniques that the various emigrants took with them when they crossed the plateau to the river valleys of India and Arabia. In any case at the time the southerly migrations took place, between 6000 and 5000 B.C., not only had the rain-bearing winds shifted further into higher latitudes but a warm and dry period of the temperate earth as a whole, known as the Thermal Maximum, began to prevail, presumably because the continental glacial masses had by this time melted away and most of the resulting water had run off the lands to become part of and raise the level of the oceans. Consequently as the neolithic people spread in search of livelihood they tended to settle where it was most easily gained, which was along the upper reaches of the rivers where they entered the alluvial plains, for here more then anywhere else some control could be maintained over the supply of water to the bordering land. The oldest villages in Arabia were along the upper parts of the Tigris—and Nineveh grew out of one of them—, along the tributaries of the Jordan—and Jericho was another; and settlements were made along the upper Nile long before the

Egyptian delta was occupied. Then as experience and populations increased, the long lower stretches of the Tigris, Euphrates and the Nile became rapidly settled by numerous small communities of irrigation cultivators, down to the edge of the tidal swamps where sea salt made farming impossible. And though we know less about it, the early history of the Indus Valley was probably the same.

You can get a sharp impression of the whole if you picture a spoked wheel. The hub represents the Caspian homelands, the rim the outer fringe of migrating explorers, and the spokes the great rivers more or less radiating from the center and along which the most permanent settlements were established. For no matter how often people themselves were displaced by newcomers from the central region, the natural advantages of the deltas and the lands behind them were so great that occupation continued uninterrupted—but for one dramatic exception, which concerns the Biblical story of the Flood.

It is a mistake to think that the earth has been slowly and steadily warming up since the end of the ice age. It did so for several thousand years until about 5000 B.C. when the Thermal Maximum or, to call it by its alternative name, the Climatic Optimum was reached. This was a period decidedly warmer than at present which lasted from 5000 B.C. to about 3500 B.C., and was moister as well as warmer than the thousand years which preceded it or the thousand or so that followed. The evidence is clear and comes from several sources: from the level of the ocean which indicated how much of the ice caps had melted, from the thickness of varve deposits laid down as annual deposits of silt, but above all by pollen grains, for the pollen grains of trees can be identified wherever they are found and however long ago they may have fallen, and once the character of an ancient forest is recognized you know what the climate must have been. Spruce and fir for instance indicate cool and moist, pine means warmer though still cool, oak and hemlock were warm and moist, oak and hickory warm and dry, a mixture of oak, chestnut and spruce cooler and moister. And in both eastern North America and northwest Europe this has been the succession since the end of the last glacial retreat until the present—the present phase in this case starting about 2500 years ago. It gives us several outstanding dates, all of them approximate: 5000 B.C. when the great migrations were under way possibly because of preceding drought, and when the river settlements to the south and west were being made; 3500 B.C. when the climate became much dried and a little cooler; and about 500 B.C. when the climate became cooler again and much wetter. Man, being a slave to water, has reacted in various ways to its presence or the lack of it, and these major climatic changes have had a potent influence.

The long, warm, humid period that lasted from 5000 B.C. or thereabouts for roughly fifteen hundred years was in its quiet and unspectacular way perhaps as fertile a stretch of human existence as there has ever been, or so it seems to me. So much began that may forever influence human destiny that I think we can hardly overestimate its importance. Irrigation farming is not the least of it, for I suspect that it will play an even more vital part in our future than it has already done in the past. The ax made plank-built boats as well as other structures possible, and paddle-driven boats became sailboats as well and the turning of a natural force to the benefit of men. Moreover I am sure it was men and not women who thought of the sail, for from the beginning all the way through the human male has been nature's greatest labor-saving mechanism: labor-saving devices in the modern kitchen only appeared after domestic help became difficult to get and the men were drafted as sparetime unpaid substitutes. And any man who has ever pulled long and hard upon an oar has put his mind to work on the possible alternatives.

We are inclined to think of men as the inventive sex as though inventiveness were theirs exclusively. I think the idea itself is undoubtedly a male invention which tends to keep females in their place both by suggestion and to a great extent by denying opportunity, yet the two sexes are equally human and given sufficient motive women can invent and create just as well as men. It stands to reason that a woman who has her heart set on producing and rearing children has little interest in tampering with an expanding universe or making atoms pop. Yet apparently women and not men started humanity upon its era of technology. Men, being primarily opportunists, took things over only after women had laid the creative foundation. There are some in fact who would assign to female inspiration and effort not only technology but agriculture and the domestication of animals as well, suggesting that the men were always out hunting and fishing. I feel this goes too far, although I suspect it is my own pride of sex that makes me feel so, for there are few males, old or young, even these sophisticated days who would not prefer to hunt or fish than sit down and tend to business.

The bottoms of the village mounds which lie scattered everywhere across the lands from the Nile to Turkestan contain the bones of domesticated animals, flint sickle blades, and broken pottery of a crude and primitive kind. For the most part the settlements were made by people who were already farmers who combined the breeding and herding of animals with the planting and reaping of grain. Flint sickles imply grain cultivation for wild grain is always harvested with a stick and basket, and sickle blades are shiny from the incessant abrasion of the silica contained in the cereal stems. The making of the sickles was in the main line of stone implement manufacture and was probably a masculine invention, but the pottery that accompanies the sickles is another matter.

Storage of food, as with most conservation practices, is an instinct and responsibility of women—as the Hopi show to this day; in fact the Hopi may well represent this early neo-lithic life transported to another continent and surviving vir-tually in its essential purity down to the present, seven to eight thousand years later than its inception in western Asia.

Grain however raised a problem. Whereas fruit and roots can always be eaten fresh, and meat can be eaten raw or roasted over an open fire, grain as grain requires very different handling, for it is hardly suitable for food as such, nor can it be readily stored except in a container. It is no coincidence, I think, that pottery and the shiny stone sickle turn up together in human time. Grain had to be ground to make meal and mixed with water to be eaten. But grain to be preserved for subsequent sowing had to be carefully stored and carefully guarded, as it is at present. So women made pots, which is more easily said than done. Vegetable gourds and simple woven baskets probably supplied the models, but the essential discovery was that vessels shaped by hand out of wet gritty clay contaminated with wood ash and dried and subsequently baked over a hot fire would retain their hardness sufficiently for grain or meal storage or for holding water. Even in its most primitive form the process is fairly complex, though the earliest kind, which spread far and wide, was relatively thick, and soft on the inside—and goes back to about 6000 b.c. in the Caspian lands. Thinner vessels baked over hotter fires made from fierce-burning thorny plants fired all the way through and covered with a painted wash of selected clay—a far superior article—appear only after 5000 b.c., and slowly traveled along the old migration routes as more people mi-grated in their turn. Shaping by hand is the simplest and the oldest method used, and throughout the world today wher-ever this method is employed, women make the pots. In many places men are prohibited from potting and among people in Assam in eastern India a man does not even speak to a woman thus engaged nor approach her work. All kinds of experimentation have gone into the mixing of the clays originally used, and also in the various procedures of drying and baking, but all of it has without any doubt been the work of women insofar as hand-wrought articles are concerned—and apart from rate of production, hand-molded pottery can be as symmetrical and beautiful as that made in other ways. Women also were the first to weave baskets and cloth from grass and from flaxen threads and eventually to create the loom, one of the most intricate inventions of mankind. Altogether, during the millenium from 5000 to 4000 B.C. in the humid warmth of the climatic optimum, women living in their small village communities laid the foundations for all the industrial ages that were and are yet to come. The oldest and the simplest loom still holds the essential patent for all of modern textile industry, while the perfection of painted pottery manufacture involved the creation of the fire kiln or furnace and the discovery of the effects of heat on the raw materials of the earth. For the first smelting of copper came accidently from the baking of clays, although the metal, either worked or poured molten into molds, was used for a long time only for the making of ornaments, which after all is the fate of all things which are bright and hard to get. Yet here the feminine motives seem to come to an end. Their concern had been for pots for storing and cooking, light-weight but durable clothing, and trinkets—but out of it eventually came the light and heavy industries of the modern world, including mining. Adobe bricks made of mud and straw, those two everpresent features of irrigation cereal farming, which in modified form we still find indispensable, we can perhaps assign to men since home construction probably always has been a male prerogative.

In any case this seems to be roughly the place where the men took over certain domestic crafts and forged the means of mobility, power and conquest. And as always the Caspian border lands and hills seem to have been the region of greatest enterprise. Why men assumed the role of the potter I do not know and cannot imagine unless the need for containers outgrew the supply and male impatience stepped in to boost the production rate. This could have been the reason since the time was one of natural abundance, or the increased demand may have arisen from the rapidly spreading custom of burying the ashes of the cremated dead in painted pots. Whatever the cause, you see the forceful drive of the male mind and personality operating at once and as clearly as at any later time. The hands of women had been fashioning pottery slowly and well for ages past, making a hole in a ball of soft clay, hollowing it out by degrees and gradually giving it the shape desired, turning the whole slowly around so that each part comes successfully into the modelling hands. No man could do it better, but by putting the mass of clay upon a flat piece of wood poised upon the end of a wooden shaft stuck in the ground and free to revolve, hand actions could be faster and pots produced in greater numbers. The revolving board became the potter's wheel mounted upon a pivot, and by spinning the wheel and assiduous practice a new and faster technique of producing pots quickly came into being. And throughout the world in all older societies where the potter's wheel is used, the potter is a man. It is a curious sex distinction, the female creating from the earth itself and holding fast to her invention, the male adding dynamics to the process and developing it in his own exclusive way.

I would not emphasize this so much if it were only a matter of making plates and pots, though pottery and its decorations reflect much of the travels, customs and personalities of historical mankind. But the potter's wheel led almost at once to the fastening of two wheels on a common shaft and putting it beneath a summer sled to make a wheeled wagon.

Oxen were already being employed to draw the wooden sleds, and the adoption of a pair of potter's wheels for locomotion reduced friction, increased speed, and led directly to the war chariot as soon as the horse was put in place of the ox. Moreover the potter's wheel led to wheels in general, to power transmission whereby the wheel was spun by a pulley worked by the foot and finally to all driven wheels, whether of autos, aeroplanes or dentists' drills.

Once men turned their hand to pottery they naturally became concerned with the efficiency of the furnace, an interest that has never died, and slowly raised the temperature within their kilns until copper and tin and other ores yielded their bright flowing metal in highly useful quantities. The basic principles of metallurgy were well worked out probably as early as 4000 B.C. and within a few centuries at the most, copper and tin were alloyed as bronze and many articles previously made of stone were cast or worked in the new metals, copper at first and later bronze. Yet neither the potter's wheel nor the metal furnace were invented in time to accompany any of the migrants that reached the Americas before the time of Columbus. The pyramids and temples of Central and South America were stonecut and neolithic from start to finish, as were the great pyramids of the Old Kingdoms of Egypt to all intent and purpose.

From 5000 B.C. to approximately 3500 B.C. the Climatic Optimum prevailed. Only the slow insidious pressures of increasing population of people and their animals expressed itself as infiltrating short-range migrations of the kind that still take place between village and village or as tribes slowly milled about. The moist millenia however appear to have come to climactic end somewhere around 3500 B.C. The legends suggest it and archaeology confirms it.

Legends are notoriously misleading, yet most have at least

a grain of historical truth and some have much more than that, so I suppose we should not be surprised to find that archaeology substantiates the biblical flood as a fact of history and as an enormous catastrophe in its time. The account in Genesis is essentially the same as the older Babylonian legend and refers to the same event, and the story was part of the oral tradition which Abraham and his followers took with them when they emigrated from the old Sumerian city of Ur on the lower Euphrates on their journey across the Syrian desert to Canaan. Yet the biblical tradition and the older Babylonian inscriptions referred to an event already dim in racial memory and it has taken excavations at Ur to bring to light the actual flood deposits and to place them in their proper time.

The Sumerian history of the Mesopotamian Valley is recorded history, for the most part inscribed upon burnt bricks since stone is lacking in the area, and the lists of kings and duration of their reigns supply a chronology, as they do in Egypt also, back to about 3000 B.C. This is approximately the oldest date given to the first of the royal tombs, but the tombs exhibit such an amazing wealth of exquisitely made articles of gold, silver, and such a fantastic and terrible ritual associated with the death of royalty that the civilization represented must have been highly sophisticated and already several centuries old. The details are fascinating but they are not relevant here. The fact that is important now is that the city of Ur which goes back somewhere between 3000 and 3500 B.C. rests upon mud which at first was thought to be the bottom of everything, the mud of the delta itself. But eight or nine feet lower down the mud disappears and the rubbish of older neolithic settlements are found, similar to those of the neighboring lands of which I have been speaking.

There is little doubt what happened. As the frail mud huts of the older people fell into decay, new ones were built over the ruins, only to collapse in turn, until what had been a low island became a hill, as elsewhere throughout the middle east. Possibly for a thousand years or more the settlement of Ur rose higher in the air as the debris of its houses piled in the streets or was flung over its walls. The people had painted hand-made pottery, reaped grain with baked sickle blades, kept the usual domesticated animals, fished in the marshes, worked a primitive loom, and towards the end at least built solid buildings of burnt brick—a highly advanced neolithic community for the time. Then came the Flood.

The eight feet of water-laid clay indicate a great depth of water of long standing. The mud of course came from the Persian hills, either as the final melting of ice and snow or more likely from rain, but the rains must have been incessant for time out of mind to have produced such a consolidated layer of clay, and while the deluge was not universal, it was at least a local disaster of the lower valley of the Tigris and Euphrates, affecting an area about the size of England. Similar legends from other regions, such as the Indus valley in Pakistan, suggest however that all the lands to the north and south of the Persian plateau were thus affected.

In any case the people of the old civilization of southern Mesopotamia who made the hand-wrought painted pottery were virtually wiped out, leaving only an impoverished and disheartened remnant. And then into the almost empty land a new race of people came down from the hills to mingle with the survivors of the old stock, bringing with them the potter's wheel and metal tools and all the latest inventions from the north. The fertile union of the new race with what was left of the old gave birth to the Sumerian civilization and a new age begins. Yet the struggle and effort required to reclaim the land after the flood waters finally receded sufficiently to make it possible is well commemorated in the creation legend of Sumer and Genesis—the 'chaos' in which the boundaries between water and dry land were still fluid, and the seemingly supernatural but powerfully human forces which separated the elements into land and water; for it was no god but the early colonists themselves who dug the channels to water the fields and drain the marshes, and so laid the foundations of the greatest of the older civilizations.

A change of climate almost always has a double impact. The drying out which made lower Mesopotamia once again inhabitable during the middle of the fourth millenium made the lands to the east of the Caspian Sea so dry as to be practically useless. And inasmuch as the people who occupied this territory were already by necessity more herders than farmers, they undoubtedly did what their successors in that region have been doing ever since under similar circumstances: they moved westward to a better place. The effect was the same as though you started to shove at the end of a queue of persons: you don't necessarily get very far yourself but the pressure passes all the way through and those at the far end are the ones who get pushed farthest out of place. The big migrations have usually been the result of displacements of a settled people by others who have had to move because their own circumstances had become intolerable, generally as the result of drought. And in the olden days particularly when any unhappy event took place it was interpreted as the wrath of the gods caused by man's own misdeeds. So that the tribes who moved south into the valley of the Tigris and Euphrates at this time carried tales of woe and punishment, having been compelled by a better armed race to leave luscious lands that they loved. Here is the expulsion from Eden and the angel with his flaming sword who stood guard against their return is the man with the bigger and better sword who had dispossessed them.

History here becomes overwhelming as humanity begins to swarm, as crafts multiply, as food becomes more abundant, and as weapons and the means of transport become more effective. As the warm dry climate replaced the warm and wet, and the resultant wave of migration more or less spent itself, the bronze age civilizations came into being and flourished wherever the new migrants with their new crafts and customs replace or mingled with the older neolithic societies. At 3500 B.C., or thereabouts, elaborate civilizations began to blossom along the course of the great rivers—in Mesopotamia along the Tigris and Euphrates and the land in between, along the lower Nile in Egypt, and in the Indus valley—and also among the islands of the Aegean Sea, with Crete as its center. Ideas and crafts and materials were freely interchanged both by land and by water, and the whole period which lasted between one and two thousand years saw the diversification of human society from emperor to slave, saw the building of the great pyramids of Egypt, the temples of Babylon, the palaces of Crete, and everywhere the employment of pictographic writing. Yet the Sumerians of Mesopotamia seem to have remained the fountain head of inspiration, supplying much that is at the root of Babylonian, Assyrian, Hebrew and Phoenician art and thought, and through them the Greeks and so finally our western civilization itself. Their influence if not their power also reached Egypt and Crete, and probably the Indus valley as well. If there was ever a golden age I think it was this, for the world was still gloriously unspoilt, the climate probably at its best from a human point of view, sail was the order of the day and adventure the rule. Just so long as we overlook the fact that the lot of the common man was that of a slave or not much better and that the privileged were few.

Yet in the long run neither the good nor the wicked are left in peace. The general dessication that was already well underway reached a climax at about 2200 B.C. throughout Europe, western Asia and Africa, and probably elsewhere, and the dry conditions prevailed, with some ups and downs, for several centuries at least. And once again those who felt the effects most were the ones to move, particularly as they had already specialized in the use of chariots now drawn for the first time by fast horses rather than asses or oxen. Since the race which now started to move away from its Turkestan homeland was illiterate little is known concerning their earlier history except that they had been living along the eastern shores of the Caspian Sea for many centuries. They were a hard and unsophisticated race and between 2200 and 1700 B.C. wave after wave in increasing power forced its way into neighboring lands, all of them speaking the mother tongue of the Indo-European language of which ours is one. One of the earlier waves spread north of the Caspian and into Europe through the Danubian corridor and also down into the Greek peninsula where in the course of time they absorbed the old Aegean civilization. This is the bronze age, Indo-European, period of Greek history so vividly left to us in Homer's epics. A later wave went slowly over the Persian plateau, where they founded the Medes and the Persians, and descended on Mesopotamia and Egypt; while the Aryan branch went over the mountains into India and destroyed the Indus valley civilization. Wherever they went they imposed their language, mingled in various degrees with the existing populations, and absorbed and developed the cultures they encountered. For they brought with them few preconceptions of their own, but an abundance of fresh blood and vigor. The infusion was greatly needed, and the tempo increases.

We have to contend with climate whether we like it or not. Usually men have moved to a better place, as the human hordes of western Asia have done every time there has been a drought. You can't blame them, although they have been a historical nuisance. But this kind of solution becomes progressively impossible as we approach the saturation point, and yet climatic change continues to bother us. We left the last major phase of the ice age behind when the ice sheets melted about ten thousand years ago. That should have been the end and we might reasonably have expected the warming up process to have continued steadily on. It didn't. Somewhere about 500 B.C. when the process of climatic cooling and drying had gone on for about two thousand years, the ice sheet covering the Arctic Ocean suddenly reappeared, possibly covering the surface in one season once it had started to form. With its reappearance the climate of the northern continents changed sharply from cool and dry to cool and wet, and it has been more or less rainy ever since. So began the Sub-Atlantic period in which we still exist. Yet its beginning coincided with the full development of the Greek City States and the dozen or so generations that gave the western world the mainspring of its civilization and climate may have been a factor directly or indirectly.

Since then it would be hard to say whether the ice is coming or going. It was relatively dry and warm in Europe during the first century A.D., and again from the fifth to the eighth when Alpine traffic became freely possible, and during this rather milder period the Irish managed to sail to Iceland, which they settled, and to the Azores, and possibly America. A little later, while conditions were almost as good, the Vikings also reached Iceland and established their Greenland colonies. Then came what has now affectionately been called the Little Ice Age. It starts with a great increase in rainfall and much storminess throughout the 13th century, the climate suddenly worsening about 1300 A.D. to such an extent that during the next three generations farming became virtually impossible in northern Europe and thousands of villages were abandoned. So was the Norse settlement in Greenland, forevermore the lost colony. But the study of pollen grains show the dismal course of climatic events during the late middle ages. That the Renaissance took place when it did is due more to the use of coal than to any climatic benediction, though the combination of a warm home in a cool climate seems to be more mentally invigorating than most. Then at the beginning of the seventeenth century there was a general advance of the glaciers, and it is only since about 1850 that they have begun to recede.

Where does it leave us? At present we are still in a phase of warming-up that may already be near its end. Great sheets of ice are beginning to break loose from the edges of Arctic islands and the ice sheet as a whole is getting thinner. It could disappear as suddenly as it came. Or we may swing back into a colder and wetter period such as the one we have just left and continue these fluctuations more or less indefinitely. All we really know is that a full scale ice age lies not very far in the past, that the ice age as a whole had three periods within it at least as free of ice as at present, that these interglacial periods lasted at least forty thousand years and one of them very much longer, and that the last cold phase is only ten thousand years past. We may be out of it for good, in which case what is left of the ice caps will eventually melt, and so raise the sea level just high enough to flood London and New York and a few other choice spots. Temperate climate will extend to the poles, which would not be particularly helpful, and the present temperate continents will become warmer and drier—to the disadvantage of water-consuming humanity. If the ice should come back in force however, which is equally possible, the tropics and the temperate zones will contract toward the equator.

The signs are ominous when we look at the most recently discovered natural recording thermometer. Cores of mud taken from the bottom of the mid-Atlantic Ocean contain the shells of minute animals that used to be alive at the surface.

The position in the core is a measure of the time when they sank to the bottom, and the quantity of carbonate they contain indicates the temperature of the sea at the time they were alive. Taken together we get a curve which shows the sea temperature from about 13,500 B.C., when the ice caps held full sway, to 1840 when the recent milder spell began. There is a steep and fairly steady rise from this beginning, through the 10,700 B.C. when the ice was on the verge of melting away, to about 6,800 B.C. when it was virtually gone. The temperature maximum appears about 4100 B.C. which is what other evidence had already shown. Then the decline begins, and the curve shows small ups and downs, with a heavy emphasis on the down beat, continuing without remission for nearly six thousand years, that is, down to the present. We are already down to the level of about 6800 B.C. and the average world temperature is therefore falling at about half the rate at which it rose between 7000 and 4000 B.C. If it continues the trend of the last six thousand years without acceleration, then in four or five thousand years the temperature becomes that which prevailed when the ice sheet was last over the site of Chicago and in ten thousand years we are back in the full grip of a glacial period. That is not a very long breathing spell and if the temperature should start to drop at the rate it originally rose, we will have perhaps no more than two or three thousand years before we face the icy blizzard, which is not so long to look ahead—less than a hundred human generations and less than the life of a redwood tree.

17

THE HUMAN CROP

MAN as an animal is just as capable of eating and breeding himself out of house and home as any other kind, and seems to be in fair way of doing so. Yet the problem is anything but new and in the past local populations often outgrew their food supply, and both in Egypt and Greece and later on in Rome efforts were made, by means of infanticide, to keep the number of human beings within bounds. Now we see the situation on a planetary scale and are even more inclined to take alarm. We have reason enough I think, for our world is in crisis in more ways than one.

It is not easy to appreciate fully the explosive quality of the human event of the last few thousand years. Nothing like it has ever happened before, not in the whole billion years of the history of life on this planet. Man the hunter remained in balance with the rest of nature just as surely as any other mammalian predator, his numbers fluctuating according to the numbers of prey within his reach and to the extent that he himself suffered from disease and other forms of destruction. Throughout the greater part of his recognisably human and subhuman history he seems to have been a rare, shy creature who used his wits to snatch a livelihood in a world where he ranked with the wolf and the bear. Only as the hunter's weapons improved toward the end of the ice age do we see any signs of potential abundance. Then the revolutions begin, with no end in sight.

Propagation of human beings during the last ten thousand years has increased prodigiously. With each change in the basis for life human numbers have surged anew. The change from the hunter communities to neolithic village agriculture or nomadic herding produced at least as great a percentage increase in the total population as has any later improvement in nutritional control. The urban revolution of the fourth millennium B.C., when the cities of Babylon, Egypt and the Indus sprang into being and irrigation farming of the delta lands and widespread trading in metals and other commodities were well advanced, saw another great expansion of humanity within those areas of civilization, an expansion which brought serfdom or slavery to the majority of the inhabitants. I doubt if we will ever know how many human beings were alive at that time, only that the totality of mankind probably lay between ten and one hundred million. But about 1650, before the age of coal and coke, the world population stood at about 550 million. Then, as the industrial revolution got under way, the total population rocketed again, so that it had doubled itself within two centuries—by 1850—, had tripled itself by 1900, and now is close to twenty five hundred million. The curve gets steeper all the time, and at present each day that passes sees some seventy thousand more babies born than were born the day before. At the present rate of increase the earth would be encumbered with five billion human beings a century from now, with even more to come. Who calls a halt, and when?

It oversimplifies the matter somewhat to speak of mankind as if it were a uniformly expanding whole, for the situation varies in different parts of the world. Yet with this in mind I believe we can make a legitimate comparison between the growth of mankind and the seeding and growth of any other kind of crop. This is no mere analogy for you and I are just as much a part of a natural self-seeding stock as any two daisies in a field. It is all a question of a food chain, one way or another, of water and fertilizer, and what else grows in the field. For in the final analysis everything that lives is a product of sunlight, water and a variety of salts, and whatever is in shortest supply limits the total quantity of living substance. This holds whether we are concerned with a meadow or a state or the earth itself. And if we want a good crop of any sort, whether it be cabbages or kings, we have to farm according to the rules.

We can look at this in two ways: what is grown and how much is grown? In terms of the human scene the first question is mainly history, the second the problem of the future.

If we switch from the model to the reality, then the original state of man was like that of any other creature in the mixed field of nature, in balance with the rest and by no means conspicuous either numerically or individually. The change from hunting to the neolithic economy was equivalent to a basic change in diet whereby human kind gained sudden access to most of the nutriment originally available for all. Competition was practically eliminated and it was only a matter of time before what was at first a diversified animal kingdom became mostly converted into living human material. The point is not subtle. Admittedly we use our domesticated animals as intermediaries, but they are captive and nothing is wasted. Man and his cattle and grain are one, and since the sum total of life has not significantly changed during the last few millenia, as humanity has grown in bulk the rest of creation has diminished. Directly or indirectly there has been a monumental and increasingly extensive conversion of the planet's living potential from the diverse many to the all-consuming one. In terms of our comparison, the virgin prairie with its stable mixture of grasses and flowers has become almost entirely corn, with a few weeds and some blowing dust. All that can be transformed into human protoplasm is being transformed, and anything that stands in the way is pushed against the wall. The wild buffalo of the plains was forced to make way for the domesticated brands; if there is to be expansion in Africa the rich and ancient fauna also must give way to cattle; deer are protected more for sport than food, but all competing predators are shot on sight, whether wolf, puma, eagle or bear. No matter who lives in the forests or among the marshes, if the wood or the land is coveted it is cut or drained—bringing disaster to the great woodpeckers, whooping cranes, trumpeter swans and their like. So far as the rest of nature is concerned we are like a cancer whose strange cells multiply without restraint, ruthlessly demanding the nourishment that all of the body has need of. The analogy is not farfetched for cancer cells no more than whole organisms know when to stop multiplying, and sooner or later the body or the community is starved of support and dies. And roughly speaking this is where we stand, having reached the ends of our domain, having filled almost all terrestrial space with human organisms, though not yet with equal density, and at last searching rather frantically for new space to conquer.

The end, such as it is, has come rather suddenly. A few generations ago the western half of the world at least was still relatively empty except for man in a state of nature; but the first colonists imported several million African slaves, while about fifty million people overflowed from Europe between 1840 and 1930. The Old World spilled into the New, reaching or pushed toward the world's last frontier. There are lesser frontiers certainly but the great wave of man's western advance has already reached the long line of the Pacific coast and shows signs of rippling back again. Where else is there to go? Free migration appears to be over, but within the continents the great central plateau of Brazil may see a major population center dominating South America, while the Russians by means of precious water diverted from the Don and Volga rivers may succeed in making the steppes of Turkestan, the original cauldron of humanity, into a new Asian civilization. In a way it would be a fitting finish, despite the fact that the pillars arise from slavery or its equivalent—for that issue is not a new one, and in any case man's use or misuse of his own kind is a challenge yet to be squarely taken.

We now cover our planet in numbers already uncomfortably great and realise I think that something has been taken from us, perhaps forever. For ages past there have been new worlds to conquer. When the old civilizations were small and more or less isolated from one another the world had no limits, adventure called and could be answered, and the great unknown stretched far beyond imagination. Travelers had tales to tell and a man could dream. Even four hundred years ago when the world already was round and fully encompassed, the seemingly empty lands of the western hemisphere called to overcrowded Europe, and always, until the present century, there was still a hazy frontier opening farther west. The restless and venturesome could still get up and go, could still reach virtually virgin wilderness where health, happiness and hope could find a home. Human masters could be left behind and man, who is essentially and incorrigibly and fortunately wild, could find his freedom and independence. In this simple and tangible form the human frontier has already gone, though so recently that most of us still feel a certain nostalgic anguish at the thought of yesterday. Until this present century, throughout the billion years of life on earth, and particularly during the million years of more or less human life, there have been frontiers beckoning like open gates to those who could venture. Now so far as I can see the gates are closed and nothing less than catastrophe can reopen them.

Yet the momentum that has carried us so far has not disappeared. Apart from the jostling pressures of increasing numbers, the wildness remains. I doubt if there is a man or a woman or a child alive who can look on high flying birds in migratory flight without some stirring of wishful envy. We seem trapped in our own backyard and long for some means of escape. How else can you account for the fact that when the New York Planetarium advertised a trip to the moon, hundreds of people mistook it for the real thing and wrote in for reservations? Or that books on interplanetary travel and so-called scientific fiction about life on other worlds are so avidly read at the present time? There is no place to go except in imagination, with the hope that the wished-for will one day come true, for our grandchildren if not for us.

Just what are the prospects? Can we sensibly hope or are we dreaming fantasies? Or must we face some agony of growth and arrive at some new stage of maturity? I fear it is the last, for while as much as anyone I like the thought that we may some day visit Mars or Venus and find them fit for occupation, all that I know is utterly discouraging.

This is a crucial matter, for in the long run it makes a great deal of difference whether we are destined to occupy other planets of the Solar System or whether this earth is all we have and all we ever will. If space travel with adequate objectives lies ahead we can postpone our maturity for a long time to come and continue to play at being superman. If not, then we face the facts of life and grow up tomorrow!

What do the other planets offer as extensions of the land frontiers that have now faded from the earth? In my opinion they offer us different forms of hell, compared with which life at the south pole, in the middle of the Sahara desert, or high on the slopes of Mount Everest would be a most welcome change. Don't forget you are two-thirds water, that you evaporate all too readily, that ultra-violet light and cosmic rays can shatter you, that oxygen is vital and that far below the level of the highest mountains there is not enough of it and not least that you have to maintain a body temperature a little below one hundred degrees Fahrenheit, no more and no less. When you find conditions which permit the existence of the warm, oxygen-saturated wetness which is you, then and only then can you start to think of a long life and the pursuit of happiness. We do well to find them on this earth, let alone on any other planet.

Water as such can itself exist within a certain range of temperature. Too close to the sun, where Mercury swings, water boils away; too far away and all is ice, which takes care of Jupiter, Saturn, Uranus, Neptune and Pluto, all of them cold enough to freeze the night. Only Venus, the Earth with its moon, and Mars lie within the belt where liquid water can exist, with the Earth in the most favored position and the other two pressing the inner and outer limits. The cosmic frontier narrows already. Yet Venus and Mars have both been fondly gazed at as the shape of things to come.

Venus, the Earth's twin sister, so alike are they in size, is only twenty-six million miles away when at its closest. Mars, thirty-five million miles away when at its nearest, is little more than half the size. Water could exist on each of them, although in a much more changeable state than we have on earth. The question is not so much one of possibility but of fact, yet so far as science can tell us the answers leave little hope. Neither water vapor nor oxygen have been detected in the atmosphere of Venus, and the thick clouds appear to be composed of dry-ice crystals swirling high in an atmosphere of carbon dioxide and hydrogen, the surface of the planet accordingly being storm-swept, bone dry and overheated, far worse than any alkali desert on the earth. Unless we have plans for reconstituting the planet itself we might as well forget about it.

Mars remains our only hope, for the moon is small, water-less and completely without atmosphere of any kind. We may land on it one day, I have little doubt, and leave behind some instruments or perhaps some poor benighted and deso-late mortals in some sort of sealed container, but except as an outlying observation post it offers little prospect. Mars, how-ever does have an atmosphere, exhibits a seasonal change in color and flaunts a couple of white polar caps, all strikingly suggestive. At one time, when imagination was stronger than telescopes, even canals were seen upon its surface. Yet none of what we now know about Mars—and we know a great deal—suggests a place that you would want to visit. If you care to cruise in outer space for its own sake, that is another matter, though one that leaves me cold.

Mars has an atmosphere, so much is certain. At the Martian surface it is about as thin as it is here at the top of Mt. Everest. Carbon dioxide is present to about the same extent as in the earth's atmosphere. Water vapor has been detected, although so far there has been no indication of atmospheric oxygen. But neither is there any sign of poisonous gases like the am-monia and methane which form the atmospheres of Saturn and Jupiter. The white polar caps are almost certainly ice or frost. Whatever they are they must be thin since they shrink and expand so rapidly with change of season. The large orange-colored areas are undoubtedly similar to our great earthly deserts, not entirely bare of some kind of vegetation for there is a seasonal change in color from greenish to reddish and back again. The faint tracks which were at first mistaken for canals appear to be several scores of miles wide and they run for hundreds of miles over the surface in a way that suggests there are no mountains or valleys. In the end, therefore, we are left with a picture of a dry planet with a limited amount of water, and with a seasonally changing vegetation which at the present time is considered to be somewhat like the lichens that cover our rocks. Yet without oxygen it is difficult to see how anything comparable to animal life as we know it could possibly exist, or how we could do very much under the circumstances ourselves even if we managed to get there.

All in all it seems to me we are on our own, on the best of all planets within the Solar system, but more lonely than before, and that the main purpose of space ships may be to get a clearer and more comprehending look at the rest of the universe—and at the same time to get a sharp and overpowering vision of the earth we live on as a little lost planet poised in emptiness beyond all understanding. My own reaction would be to dive for home and pull the trees close over my head.

So far as I can see there is no place left to go that merits the journey except those parts of our own planet already within our grasp. We have even been to the poles, to the tops of the highest mountains, and are about to reach the greatest depths of the oceanic abyss—all vicariously, I know, but for such trips as these that is enough for most people. The restriction and the sense of loss are real; the first must be accepted and the heart ache I suppose will pass with time and eventually be forgotten. Henceforth we move in new dimensions.

If this then is our fate, to live for near eternity upon this earth or else not to live at all, then we need to take stock of our present situation. The western hemisphere taken as a whole is not yet saturated with human beings, although locally, as in Puerto Rico and certain metropolitan centers, the congestion is appalling. In Europe, excluding its warmer and more passionate parts, while the population is dense there is a fair balance between birth and death. In Asiatic Russia there is an abundance of land though poor conditions for human life, but there is room for a much larger population under certain circumstances, a statement I suppose which applies equally to subarctic North America and to the arid regions of Africa and Australia. In both India and China and adjacent lands however we find one half of the total population of mankind living on less than one fifth of the earth's land surface. Sooner or later, if spawning humanity keeps on the way it is going, saturation will be universally attained, and the all-important question will be how much of a load can the earth carry, how much seed can we sow and still produce healthy stock? Inasmuch as we are animals with all the nutritional needs of animals the question is legitimately put in terms of stock-raising, and since all stock, whether wild or tame, feeds upon what is or has been vegetation, we finally get down to the grass roots.

Human requirements fall into two rather different categories: sources of energy whereby we can perform work far beyond the capacity of our muscles, and sources which not only energize the individual human organism but supply the qualitative chemical basis from which human substance can be grown. In the present connection the first of these is the less important. We are burning up the fossil fuels—coal and oil—at a crazy rate primarily for the energy they contain, and we are about to exploit the atomic energy stored in uranium ores just about as recklessly. These are capital expenditures that can last for only a limited time, longer than my lifetime or yours it is true but not so long that children still carrying your name and mine will be taught to look back on our age as the age of waste. Yet there are indications already that we may be able to store energy received directly from the radiation of the sun, and this in years to come may serve as an adequate substitute for what we now throw to the winds every time we start a car or turn a switch. We may have more or less to play with— it is anyone's guess—and frankly I don't care. If I thought the gasoline age was to be the permanent pattern I would resign from the race here and now, for too much time and effort has gone into the making of men for this present technological monstrosity to be the climax. I hope, in our present phase, we are merely a passing and unpleasant phenomenon in a long and unfinished adventure into time.

Our numerical limits however are set by other factors than our access to sources of free energy. Always in the past and apparently always in the future we come back to the land. Sea salts still flow in our blood but our bones come from the soil itself, for dust unto dust is no idle image and it is time we faced the facts of life. The greatest of these is phosphorus. In the form of phosphate, mainly of calcium, it is more than the fertilizer you add to your garden, more than the toughness of your bones or the hard enamel of your teeth, it is the power of your muscle and the force of your brain. It is essential to life itself, not just the structural supports but to the delicate yet powerful energy transfers that make all living substance different from the non-living so-called inanimate world that gives it birth.

Other elements besides phosphorus are equally vital but they are either present in relative abundance or a shortage has less disastrous effects. Phosphorus dominates the situation because it is absolutely essential to life and is in short supply. Soil may lose its fertility because of exhaustion of nitrates withdrawn by the crops, but nitrates can be replaced by soil bacteria or by human ingenuity from the inexhaustible nitrogen in the air. But when the phosphates are gone they can be replaced only by human action, and they do not come from an immeasurable reservoir but from certain deposits in the earth's crust of very limited extent. When these are used up, as they are likely to be at the present rate within a foreseeable future, we will have no other source beyond what already lies diffused in the soil except that which is even more diffused in the oceans of the world. We may become desperately put to extracting phosphates from the sea but the cost would be unbelievable and if we took it from the more accessible surface layers it would to a great extent be robbing our own bread basket. For the uppermost layers also have their own limitations of supply and the so-called bread basket of the sea that contemporary visionaries are hopefully contemplating as a panacea is equally restricted in bulk by available phosphorus.

It matters, and it matters a lot. It matters particularly for two reasons: because natural replacement of phosphate deposits, any more than those of coal and oil, cannot take place within a period of time that has real significance for us. Although the question remains, if these deposits could be formed once, why not again? Perhaps they can, but we can't wait. Coal for instance was laid down for the most part between two and four hundred million years ago as the pollen grains of tree fern forests settled in the swamps and became consolidated. Oil is probably still being formed as in the past from the settling and compression of single celled plants sinking from the surface to the beds of shallow seas, and wherever you find oil, whether in the Arabian desert or in the belt that runs from the Gulf of Mexico to the Canadian prairies, you know that shallow continental seas once swept across these areas. But drilling deep for oil is like drilling into time itself, and the oil we now use is the accumulation from an even longer stretch than that of coal. Even at that we can drill, except for the tidelands, only where the land has lifted sufficiently to become free of the seas that once covered it. Neither the magnitude of time nor the events themselves can be measured against the human scale, and the same applies to phosphates. Phosphate deposits have also been found beneath the sea and subsequently lifted up by foldings of the earth's crust to a level where we can get at them, and once again there will be no more laid down in human time. The implications of this are manifold yet at the base is the hard fact of phosphate limitation. There is no possible substitute and there is a limited quantity available for the production and maintenance of life, not just human life but all life.

To begin with it means that we cannot markedly increase

the fertility of the earth, except temporarily by spending capital deposits, and that present day chemists who confidently scoff at the misgivings of conservationists and protagonists of human population control have never fully faced the issue. Science, especially at its technological level, has performed such miracles during the recent past that its practitioners have to a notable degree acquired a superman complex —no human problem is beyond their capacity to solve—and the public is inclined to take them at their own valuation. Some of the harshest diatribes which followed publication of 'The Road to Survival' came from chemists who objected to the fact that it was written by a conservationist who was also an ornithologist, I suppose basically because their role as omnipotent human engineers was being sharply challenged. Of course the sense of accomplishment is wonderful and it hurts to think there may be a limit and that the present may not be a prelude to bigger and better things. Better they certainly should be, but no bigger. Activities tend to get out of hand and there is intoxication in the grandiose. The bigger the dam and the more nature is flaunted and bent to human direction, the greater the desire to repeat it on a larger scale. Unfortunately the same inclination is too readily transferred to manipulating human beings, so that mankind itself is regarded as the raw material, in addition to inarticulate and inanimate nature, for man-made experiments. Live puppets are always more fun to play with, as any child knows.

I do not believe that the carrying capacity of the earth will ever be much greater than it is now. The total amount of life both on the land and in the sea, is more or less fixed by circumstances beyond our control. All that we can decide, and the decision is neither easy to make nor comfortable to live with, is the ratio of this kind of life to that kind of life within the total. Apart from this our concern is to make the best of what there is—and belatedly since the human impact upon the land during the last two or three thousand years has been far from good. Ever since we have existed in significant numbers, carrying an ax in one hand and driving a goat with the other, we have been cutting down forests, killing saplings, grazing far too close, causing the rain or melting snow to run off the land much too fast, carrying top soil and all that it contains down to the sea in ever-increasing quantity. Soil and sewage enrich the sea but impoverish the land, while the phosphates in our bones we carefully put out of circulation in our ever-expanding cemeteries. Dust should be returned to dust and is too valuable to be washed into the sea or embedded in a coffin. When you live on a budget there are certain luxuries you cannot afford, and the luxury of waste is the most expensive. Between the minerals of the soil and the rain that reaches them we find our limits. We work within them.

In the future which is almost upon us the problem of over-population looms very large. In parts of the world it is already serious and before very long the problem will be a general one for all mankind. There are only three possibilities, which is a dangerous way of speaking since nature so often seems to put a queer twist into the scheme of things. One is that we can increase our resources indefinitely to keep pace with the increasing population, which I have tried to show is impossible. Another is that we employ our collective intelligence and keep our numbers within reasonable bounds, while the third is the pessimistic one that human beings are not intelligent enough as a whole to control their own fertility and will always press hard against the ragged fringe of sustenance. If we wish to see the shape of our destiny this last must be taken as a definite possibility which in the long run is a more serious threat to all that we value most than any atomic war. If such is to be our fate it means we are already approaching the end of our tether, for never in the past has a race survived which failed to make necessary adjustments to changing circumstances.

The argument is that limitation of population is necessarily an unstable process which cannot persist for long and that for the next million years or for as long as we can last the path of mankind will simply be that of the history of China, only on a world-wide scale. That always the more fertile or the more prolific human strains or races will outbreed the rest, that population control by any group sooner or later seals its own doom, with those who retain an uncontrollable breeding instinct taking its place. That always there will be relapses into barbarism in various parts of the world with civilizations persisting here and there serving to infect the new growth wherever it arises; that in most regions and most of the time population pressure will be intense, with periodic famine and a callousness towards human life that comes from having too many people, such as we see in China today. Essentially it would be the present situation intensified and indefinitely prolonged, with always a minority living at a high esthetic and material level and the great majority miserable and undernourished if not actually oppressed. The prospect is a dismal one and it is not for such as this that the earth and the sun exist.

I have more faith in the essential humanity of man. I believe that the so-called common people of the world are more innately intelligent and more instinctively wise than the rulers of state and church and other self-styled elect are willing to credit. That lack of real intelligence and comprehension is more rampant among those who would govern than among those who have no such inclination; for the assumption that ordinary men and women do not know what is good for them and must be told what to do or what not to do suggests a degree of conceit and self-righteousness that no man is entitled to.

Population control means birth control. Why the idea or the practice should arouse such emotional opposition I find difficult to understand. It is as though nothing must be done to interfere with the course of nature, no matter where the course of nature leads, and as though we have been interfering with nature in no other way. No technique of control is at present entirely satisfactory but I have little doubt that one that is will be discovered before very long. And in so far as it becomes generally available I have no doubt at all that womankind will adopt it. In overcrowded Japan and in swarming India where the crisis is already acute, with worse to come, the need for sensible adjustment of people to resources is so great that controls are already officially encouraged; while even in Mexico, in spite of church edicts to the contrary, a movement spreads to keep human beings in balance with the land. Given the freedom to choose, and the means, human beings everywhere and particularly the women who bear the brunt of child bearing and rearing are anxious to raise children with a chance for health and happiness—no one cares to see the majority of infants die of disease or chronic starvation, which is the state of affairs prevailing throughout the orient, and neither does the human species have any need of this particular form of natural selection, which is not the selection of any worthwhile human traits. Sooner or later I think human societies everywhere will adopt some feasible method of birth control which will permit populations to remain in a steady state with births and deaths equalized as far as possible and mankind as a whole to remain numerically in balance with the earth that sustains it. Only then will we have accepted our heritage in the spirit in which it is offered.

The greatest adjustments we will ever have to make will be in order to live with ourselves. For when an individual or a nation or human society as a whole makes an irreversible decision, the consequences must be accepted for better or for worse. And once the decision is generally acclaimed that human numbers be kept within certain limits and that every individual shall have the greatest possible chance to live to a healthy old age, certain consequences follow as surely as day follows night.

18

GROWING UP

Mankind is growing up, with all the pain and anguish that comes with the passing of youth and the assumption of responsibility for self-direction. The process is as complex and difficult as any other form of maturing, and like all such is a culmination. In this case the twentieth century sees the inevitable climax of the long process which began with the neolithic revolution eight to nine thousand years ago. All that has gone on in the meantime, all that was set in incipient motion when human beings first dug their heels into the ground and anchored themselves to the soil is rapidly coming to fruition. And when everything comes to a head at once the outcome is another revolution. There have been stages in between, the bronze age, the iron age, the coal and gunpowder age, and in the same line the atomic age. These are all technological steps in an essentially continuous process, each of which has had a tremendous influence upon the fate of nations but none of which by itself can be called revolutionary. Gunpowder and steel swords have been as deadly in their own time as atom bombs threaten to be now. In other ways other technological phenomena have been influential.

The neolithic change forced women to stay at home and spend much of their time squatting while they ground grain or shaped pots; when men took over pottery making they too squatted at their work and also devised the potter's wheel; and from that point on chairs on the ground and chairs on wheels have increasingly substituted for a good pair of legs, so that we are in fair way to sit out most of our working life either over or behind a wheel or in a chair that becomes progressively more reclining. Again it is not revolutionary by itself, any more than the climax we seem to be approaching in the matter of transportation, when every part of the planet is put within a few hours flight of every other. In every case we come to a place where any further procession in the same direction will make relatively little difference to the general picture—to be able to cross the Atlantic overnight is epoch-making, but to do so in half the time does not markedly change the situation.

Yet there is one progressive change which is culminating with the rest which would alone suffice to transform the human society, and much of what we loosely call our standard of living is wrought up with it. It goes hand and hand with population control and once we recognize the limits of the earth and at the same time insist that every baby born should if possible live out his or her three score years and ten, then we have an inescapable state of affairs which is new in our corner of the universe. It is the change from a human society composed mainly of adolescents and young adults to one consisting for the most part of fully mature individuals.

Throughout human history everywhere until about a century ago human beings have been reproducing as rapidly as possible, as a rule as often as a child is weaned, which in the less civilized races at least is after two or three years. But of the children produced the vast majority have died in infancy or childhood and only the favored few survived to attain the wisdom of old age. Montaigne in the sixteenth century wrote that he rarely met a man as old as fifty. A birth rate close to the biological maximum has been necessary to maintain a growing population in the face of an appalling rate of infant mortality and the famines and epidemics that periodically decimated human societies. Europe during the middle ages when the black death swept the continent time and time again was no wit better than the Roman Empire of an earlier time or China and India in recent years. This has been the pattern throughout the ages, not merely of human time but for all nature and for the whole period of life on earth. Every animal and plant throughout creation has been busy producing their special offspring at the greatest possible rate, with oblivion as the fate of the less successful. Perhaps this is the underlying reason why we seem so reluctant to put brakes upon the process in our own case, the instinct is ingrained so deeply that intelligence can hardly reach it.

Yet here is the rub I think, for we generally overlook the reason for such a compulsive urge, which is to keep a credit balance in the fight of life against death. When we have virtually won the battle by means of sanitation, public health, and the whole armory of modern medicine and other resources, as we have already in the western world, everything is changed. Instead of the forces of premature death fighting furiously against an insuppressible stream of life, death in its old-fashioned guise has been vanquished—though not yet everywhere. Most of the great human expansion of the last century or two has been the result of more people living longer, and not of any increase in rate of production. In the west the process of adjustment is well advanced and birth rate and death rate are slowly coming into balance on the new terms. In the east not only are numbers already almost astronomical but birth and death are still in furious combat. The immediate danger as I see it is that as public health improves and the average age of the populations rise, the pressure of expanding humanity will become tremendous before there is time for the birth rate to become adjusted. In any case the comparison which we can make between China and North America or Europe at the present time shows the past and future state of societies in sharp and enlightening contrast, at least in a general way.

The old societies were youthful societies and still are wherever they survive. The average life expectancy is thirty or less, the result of high mortality in the first and fifth decades of life. The bulk of the population lies in the resilient teens and the reproductive twenties and thirties. Early death is over-familiar, human life readily expendable, armies readily recruited, and the long view of life, when individual life is so short and precarious, too easily lost. Such have been the races that have swept in waves across the earth and battled against each other for land worth living on.

In the west the shape of things to come is already upon us. In the United States and Canada and elsewhere, such as Denmark and New Zealand, where the same type of society is found, the average life span is already about sixty eight and still slowly rising to approximate the biblical value. It means that the vast majority of human beings living in the western communities now survive into their eighth decade and die from actual breakdown of the body resulting from age rather than disease, malnutrition or violent death, highway accidents notwithstanding. At present there are about thirty three million people in the United States between the ages of forty-five and sixty-four, and about thirteen million who are older than that. By 1980 the Department of Labor predicts that forty-three million will be between forty-five and sixty-four and as many as twenty-two millions will be older than the generally accepted retirement age. And unless we cease to strive for a peaceful world and also give up our effective control of infective disease the trend will continue. Whether we like it or not the average age of the human population will continue to rise, both here and eventually everywhere, and somehow we have to adjust our way of life to make the best use of the whole and not merely the first half or two thirds of it. When nearly one half of the population is of an age to be aware of its losing fight with the force of gravity, with arches falling and muscles sagging, when youth is in everyway more precious, war will be a matter for all or none and wisdom may prevail. Families cannot be large nor children relatively numerous in such a society, for otherwise we are off again on the same old runaway as we were before. We will be faced, as we are already beginning to realise, with more time on our hands than we know profitably how to use. The ultimate consequences are immense and hard to estimate and raise the problem of the individual human in its most intense form. Meanwhile there are other phases of the present revolution that concern us.

In spite of artificial barriers to international trade and travel, in spite of national efforts to block international broadcasts, the human world is in process of becoming one. Who or what dominates it may be in question, but the oneness is assured. We know in our minds that the planet has shrunken and however we may act we know that all societies are interdependent and that events in any part will affect the whole; and in our hearts we know that all men are brothers and our greatest need is to understand each other, that there is but one kind of man, whether light or dark, simple or sophisticated. All of this is clearly known and much of the present turmoil and tension comes I think from belated efforts to hold back the clock, to gain advantage before time runs out. Yet time has run out and henceforth so far as I can see we will have to live with our neighbors and like it. But for a while at least the closer we are the louder the squabble.

Look for a moment at the way we have come. Before the last glacial advance of the ice age there were men in Africa, Europe and Southern Asia. They could talk after their fashion, hunt with weapons and maintain fire—they were truly men but they were more diverse than we are now and only some of them survived. If this was the first phase of fully human history the second was the later emergence of a single human species in the narrow sense of the term, a single type, in spite of superficial appearances to the contrary, which spread from the Eurasian heartland to the far corners of the earth. The third phase started with the neolithic agricultural revolution. Here began the population rise that threatens us now with standing room only, and the increase in rate of transportation that makes crossing or traveling on a highway a deadly risk. It saw the start of the exploitation of the land, the first man-made erosions, cuttings and diggings that are slowly scraping away the green cover and sustaining soil to expose the earth's bare bones. It saw the change from a state of society in which all men were free to run and hunt, in which wisdom but not wealth could be accumulated, to one where land became property, grown grain and captive animals solid wealth, and where the few began to grow rich and the many became poor. Capitalism, so productive of both good and evil, started then and so did many other things. The first small scattered villages grew larger and more numerous and so began the withdrawal from the state of nature. Men who had run with the wind as part of the flowering earth withdrew into settlements and put a screen between indoors and outdoors and drew a line between the land they now considered to be theirs and the wilderness to which they had previously belonged. The wild became rural and then urban as the more favored villages grew into towns and at last to cities anyone of which now houses almost as many human beings as were alive on the earth when the process began.

There is a limit to all things—which may be trite but is nonetheless true. There is a limit to bigness, a limit to speed, a limit to numbers and a limit to complexity—not theoretically, which is in the realm of imagination, but practically in the sense that beyond a certain limit the penalty for further advance is greater than the advantage. And it is this general condition we are rapidly approaching.

Our cities drain the countryside and like all transplanted tissues tend to die at the heart while forever spreading like a malignant growth from the edges—requiring fantastic commutations on the part of hapless inhabitants who are supposed to be in two places at once, and making easy escape into any semblance of the natural world a near impossibility. We are in serious danger of losing our birthright altogether.

Speed at least at the surface has already passed reason; and human numbers even where they have not yet become an embarrassment are generally irritating—for unless you can climb a mountain or sail far out to sea it is virtually impossible to find true solitude where you no longer see a human face or hear a human voice. There is a need for it, for a universe exists beyond our towns and beaches which can be sensed only without distraction or thought of mankind. Once upon a time a man could withdraw into the desert for forty days to find his God. Now it takes some sore of planned expedition to get there, and the chances are that ten other souls will have had the same desperate idea.

Yet because of our increasing worldwide propinquity, in terms of communication if not personal intermingling, the regional cultures which have sprung into being at different times during the last seven thousand years have each reached their limits as separate and distinctive manifestations. East and west are now reaching far into each others collective minds, insidiously perhaps, but definitely. The pools of thought which accumulated wherever early civilizations grew—in Mesopotamia, Egypt, India, and China—have flowed together in time, spreading through Greece and the whole of the west, and now embrace the human world in spite of iron and bamboo screens. The fusion of the currents is incomplete and the eddies are strong, but the waters are one. A unified but not uniform world culture is in the making, and the present schizophrenia is more assumed than real.

The greater danger to human welfare comes I think from tendencies inherent in communist and free-world societies alike, rather than from the politics of power. Russia and the west are driving in the same direction, although each in its own wagon, and the ultimate peril which confronts us is the same whether one or the other or both together succeeds in dominating the earth.

There is a drive in the affairs of men which leads on to a seemingly inevitable end, like a ruthless process of unfolding development leading from a seed to some monstrous all-consuming organism. We seem to be caught in the compounded motion of all we have ever done, swept forward by forces to which all men have contributed but which no man controls, helpless in the grip of an emerging superstate.

Everything seems to be converging at once. Sheer numbers produce a general density of population. Increasing convergence produces ever-widening centers of local congestion. The two together demand an increasing complexity of transportation, public services of all kinds, and of local government. International and interregional commerce and cooperation require ever-increasing elaboration of centralized controls, so that bureaucracy is already overbloated and suggests the tail that wags the dog. The state becomes overgoverned by cumbersome departments, by lawmakers who must forever go on making laws whether they are needed or not, by petty officials in union, government and business alike whose concern is to tell people all the way down the line to do something they probably prefer not to do. Yet pervading it all is a technology that tends even to usurp the functions of the state itself, a technology rapidly becoming world-wide in type and incessantly growing larger and increasingly diverse. The production line becomes the major symbol of our time, with each final product demanding a fantastic sustaining organization, with production, plus some profits, becoming an end in itself irrespective of genuine consumer needs. Each manufacturing system of elaborate machinery and human organization becomes something which seems to parody life, a dynamic thing which must be kept alive and if possible growing at all costs, irrespective of the rate of consumption of raw material and the rate of discard of the finished product. Humanity itself, in large part at least, together with all the natural resources of the earth is being drawn into the loom of a materialistic and overlarge technological civilization until the whole world takes on the semblance of a planetary industry. The vital question is what will be the consequences?

If we simply take the process of growth of human society, particularly in its technological setting, and project it into the future the prospect is disturbing. It makes little difference whether we look forward a century or two or as much as a thousand years or even much longer—in any case we are considering the fate of our descendants inasmuch as they will be the individuals who will actually be alive at the time. On the other hand I believe that insofar as we become conscious of the past we assume a responsibility for the future and in a real sense participate in it even though as individuals we soon fade away. Several efforts have been made during the present century to forecast the state of society on the assumption that we continue the way we have been going, from the Wellsian Utopias in the early years to Orwell's terrible '1984' and more recently in Seidenberg's 'Posthistoric Man.' In all of these the state, technology and material welfare predominate, with the individual becoming progressively more and more a cog in the machine. The superstate in one form or another takes all and gives all, taking the life out of nature and the soul out of

man and giving material security to those who contribute un-
questioningly to the vast super-organism. Human beings, most
of them, assume the role of bees or termites in insect society.
Between the two of them in fact we can see something of our
reflection: the fate of most termite societies is to grow until
they eat themselves out of hearth and home, consuming their
immediate world until it falls apart; while bees, marvelously
well equipped with skills and senses, almost miraculously so
when you consider their small size, follow a changing and complex pattern of instinctive behavior throughout each short life,
perfectly adjusted at all times to the needs of the hive as a
whole. It is instinctive living at its best, which we can admire
but want no part of. Yet here is the problem, can we attain a
comparable perfection of society and of organized behavior
while retaining all the essential qualities that make man
human?

Not without a struggle, and possibly not at all, which is
what makes the present state of Russia and the picture '1984'
so repugnant. At certain stages and in some regions more than
others coercion is and will be required to force the multitudes
into lines dictated by the few, and if not coercion then by seduc-
tion—the outcome can be equally unfortunate. Judging from
the direction we have taken since the start of neolithic times
we are moving inexorably toward a world state in which we
hope the brotherhood of man will be at least a dominant note.
But what kind of men will be brothers?

If we continue to drive toward one single supernational
organism comparable to the insect society but in our own time
and on a planet-wide scale we shall be merely following the
general rule that seems to represent the trend in both evolving
matter and evolving life—to pass from the simple to the complex, from low degrees of organization to higher and higher
levels of differentiation and controls. Why should evolving
human society be excepted, particularly when it seems to have

traveled already so far along the road? We may not wish to reach a permanent state elaborate beyond our imagination but forever after unchanging but we may not have any choice. At least this is one prediction which must be taken seriously. Organization and order demand and breed more organization and more order, and human society as a whole becomes an enormous bureaucracy directing the lives and maintaining the industry of a staggering population, with each individual life controlled and protected from the cradle to the grave. The welfare state is here already and the thought of its extension to all of mankind cannot easily be brushed aside.

The stake is human intelligence. To maintain the whole fantastic structure a high degree of intelligence becomes essential at the top levels, pure intelligence devoid of feeling and capable of ruthless action, with the qualities of the politburo; while at all lower levels docility and low intelligence combined with skill and the absence of emotion are required for frictionless operation. This might be the final state continuing indefinitely, or it might lead to a further crystallization of society in which all is subordinated to the perpetuation of a super-organism in which a small collective intelligence alone survives as a controlling center, while the mass performs its functions for the most part instinctively, without thought, without emotion, or even significant consciousness of self— a wonderfully complex but essentially dehumanized society. Theoretically even the controlling intelligence might in the course of time operate instinctively. Insect societies reached such a state more than one hundred million years ago, so why not ours? There is no end of time ahead for such as this to happen.

At the base of it all lies the problem of the individual and the state, to give society its more ominous label, and in the end the individual wins. And again it is a question of intelligence. Science fiction, from H. G. Wells' 'Time Ma-

chine' to the present spate, has often pictured this crystallization of human society as a rigid unchanging existence controlled by reason and supplied by infinite scientific knowledge,
in which the ruling caste is a closely inbred intelligent race and
the rest a subspecies of industrious robots. But the means by
which such a splitting of the race could take place is never
discussed, I suppose because no difficulty is seen since in a
general way like breeds like. Yet breeding for intelligence is a
vastly difficult enterprise which requires a large population
at all times and cannot be maintained within a limited ruling
group without running into loss of vigor, fertility and many
other detrimental qualities. Fortunately this appears to be one
idea that nature has not provided for and which we have no
particular cause to fear. In this sense we are all in the same
boat and we cannot readily raise the level of intelligence of the
few without doing so for the many. On the other hand if the
smooth running of a technological superstate is dependent
upon the contented existence of vast multitudes of men and
women of low intelligence, the loss of intelligence will show
at the top as well as the bottom—and without either high
intelligence or perfected instincts available, the system col-
lapses and crumbles under its own mass. There are already signs
that our general level of intelligence is incapable of coping
with the problems of organization that already exist. In fact
any course we take which encourages or even permits a lessening
of intelligence is an invitation to extinction. We arrived at our
present eminence because we were more intelligent than our
nearest human relatives, while they became extinct. And I
doubt whether in the long run the need for intelligence has in
anyway decreased—we keep up standards or we perish. Perhaps in a hundred million years the intelligent descendants
of rats will be digging into some curious leaden caskets containing a little organic dust, and chewing their tails in intellectual frustration. It is no more impossible than what did

happen during the last hundred million years. Only the individual in this world is short of time, and even as a species we could leave our mark upon the earth without leaving a human soul to see it.

I do not believe that we have either the degree or the kinds of intelligence necessary to run a gigantic planetary organization along the lines of a bigger and better bureaucracy, and I cannot imagine anything more stultifying than such an undertaking. But how far we will press the attempt through sheer momentum before human intelligence asserts itself and says this is not the way, I do not know. The decision may be forced upon us sooner than we expect.

Excessive numbers alone may introduce difficulties much faster than we can overcome them, but it is nature herself who finally calls the turn. The fundamental problem is one of bigness, excessive bigness which is simply the product of unrestrained growth, although the size of anything is determined by factors outside its own control. Sooner or later, and probably sooner rather than later, we will have exhausted phosphate deposits and the accumulation of fossil fuels. When that time comes we can count our numbers in terms of how much of the limiting chemicals there are left to be shared among us and how much an individual requires—not too easy to ascertain but nevertheless a mathematical outcome which is variable only within a certain relatively small range. My own guess is we will be considerably less numerous than the present, possibly much less, and certainly not some significantly greater number. I realise that no small element of wishful thinking enters here, yet all I know as a biologist concerning the course of growth of animal populations which are free of predators and dependent on a basic vegetation for sustenance confirms it. I cannot see how mankind alone can cheat the fundamental rules of growth. And when the fossil fuels have almost all been burnt and the little that is left has become far too valuable to be used simply as a source of energy, what then?

Atomic energy is the quick answer, yet uranium ores are just as limited a stock and as readily exhausted as the fossil fuels, and in any case this kind of energy may be one we shall have to renounce for vital reasons. Which leaves us as free energy for heat or power only what we can get directly from the sun's radiation, from the water-power of rivers and tides, and from the combustible fuel we can grow as a crop. And not only this. We cannot forever go on mining the earth as we are doing for so many materials we think we need without reducing supplies to the point where it no longer pays to go on. In the end we come down to earth and live according to our earthly income and not according to an inheritance from all the past which we have claimed and used as though it were ours and only ours.

When there is no end to foreseeable time or, within reason, to the existence of the earth as a planet fit for habitation, a few hundred or even a few thousand years here or there make little difference and whatever the more immediate future may hold I believe we eventually come to terms with the planet—in greater wisdom, humility, and appreciation of what we are, how we came to be, and a better sense of values and purpose. If we are intelligently wise, and that is the primary condition of our continuing presence here on earth, we will cherish the earth, keep our numbers to a value good for man and land alike, conserve all resources whether animal, mineral or vegetable, and retain and develop only such technology and organization as may be compatible with wisdom.

At present and for the near future I believe we are experiencing the culminating phase of the neolithic excursion and are more than slightly intoxicated from the picnic. The whole event needs to be seen in perspective, not merely as itself but in relation to the whole human and prehuman past. We should never lose sight of the fact that the slow growth of the human brain with its manifestations of mind and spirit during the last million years has occurred within a thinly scattered numerically weak population. Man as a hunter or as a primitive food gatherer has never been numerous and for most of the time has been a rare creature. Only with the change of life which came with the invention of agriculture did humanity assume the character of a locust plague. It seems to me that we can picture our past up to the beginning of neolithic times as a small group of climbers laboriously climbing the precipitous slopes of a high mountain, with one after another falling to death as the hazards increased. Then far from the top, on a wide mountain meadow in the lush warmth of unexpected sunshine, the survivors relax, forget about the climb and settle down for good, or they so think, in a garden of Eden in which they busily propagate their kind. It has been a nice interlude, but the garden is getting full and we have spread out horizontally almost to the limit. We look down over the heights our somewhat remote ancestors have climbed and begin to realize there are also heights above us which can give us a far wider and deeper view of the universe than that we can see from here. The analogy is not too far-fetched. The essence of man is his quality, not his quantity, and this is no place to stop, halfway between ape and angel.

19

ATOMS AND GENES

U NLESS an atomic war
should so destroy civilization that all cultural and technological
continuity with the past is lost we will have to live with our
discoveries and make the best of them. I suppose a common
point of view would be: in heaven's name why not? Yet it is
a pity, I think, that the products of our imagination must
always be put to immediate application. No one lived more in
an ivory tower than the nuclear physicist of twenty and thirty
years ago, no one more innocently played mathematical games
with the known properties of elements, and in the end I think
no one was more shocked that a purely intellectual insight into
the nature of matter should be seized and turned into a threat
of universal destruction, even though the leading intellects
themselves, under intangible but powerful pressures, were
foremost in the deadly exploitation of their minds. And nowhere in the scientific world has there been such evidence of
revulsion and feeling of guilt as occurred after the first atomic
explosion. The issues go deep, for no individual is free from
the society of which he is a part, and western society as a
whole assumes the responsibility and seems to realise it. Con-

science makes cowards of us all, and having cast the first bomb we live in fear of the fear we have evoked, forever watching the skies for what we were the first to throw. Western men proclaimed the rights and the brotherhood of man, but their voices were silent or unheard in discussions of military expediency. More recently even lack of enthusiasm for extending the potential scope of atomic death to unlimited dimensions has been branded a social sin under certain circumstances. And Government, it was said, has the right to search the soul of a man. It has not! It may have the power, but it has not the right, and only a selfrighteous complacency or a cold cynicism could claim it.

Who threw the first stone may be a moral issue, but the fact remains that something was shattered and we may be never the same again. The threat of atomic destruction hangs over our heads, perhaps for ages to come, and we shall have to live with it and get used to it, going about our affairs like the citizens of Pompeii within the shadow of Vesuvius hoping the worst will never happen and acting as if it won't.

Yet Vesuvius did blow up and atom bombs may fall whatever measures we may take to prevent them or to make the unthinkable seem impossible. What then? It depends to some extent on how long we stockpile before hurling our missiles across the earth. If intelligence fails after a divided world has acquired a full atomic arsenal, which is a greater danger than the immediate one, we wake up to an aftermath far worse than that in Wells' 'Shape of Things to Come' where human wolf-packs sought survival among the wreckage. The foremost casualty would be all that depends upon complex organization, the greatest chaos appearing where there had been most to destroy, whether as cities, industries or just people. I can see little use in either trying to dodge the blast if it comes or making serious plans to pick up the fragments afterwards. The stake here is not so much the cities or even civilization—in the long run they are expendable—but humanity itself.

If we set our minds to it we could probably slaughter nine-tenths of mankind and still find a well populated world after the lapse of some centuries, like a forest regenerated after a fire, although the pattern of society would have changed. But the horror of atomic war is far more than the reign of death and misery it would bring. It is the threat to all posterity and not even to that of man alone. I do not suppose it would mean the end of planetary life, even human; but most of surviving mankind and much of the animal life and the earth's vegetation would be so affected where it matters most that future generations would exhibit increasing degrees of abnormality and would eventually disappear—monsters inheriting the worst consequences of biological sin. Yet the planet is tough and so is man and probably here and there a few healthy breeding stocks living in regions relatively uncontaminated by radio-activity would survive and in the course of millennia give rise to a new humanity with only a misty memory of the old and without the same old easy resources for making mischief. Man would still be man, with all his potentiality, but he wouldn't be your descendents or mine, either genealogically or culturally, but might well stem from pygmies in the Melanesian islands or from some other group equally unconsidered as representative of the contemporary world. If this should be the course we run and mankind eventually regenerates from some small non-typical fragment of the present terrestrial population, how would you regard it? I can see no alternative but to think we would still live, just as Neanderthal man and the Cave painters still live in us although we are most likely not of their seed.

Yet even if the bombs are held in leash we still are in the atomic age and the same danger remains, only in a more insiduous form. Atomic test explosions have already brought the lesson home. For whether by explosions or by carelessness with wastes produced as by-products of peaceful exploitation of atomic energy, we are all set to increase the radioactivity of the atmosphere, the soil and the seas to levels far above anything living organs previously have had to tolerate. For in view of the pollution that industry and city communities have already produced what possible assurance can we have that no radioactive waste will be let loose to plague us? The burns which Japanese fishermen received from the 'fall out' many hundreds of miles from a hydrogen bomb explosion were startling because of the distance and their grisly nature. But much more sinister are the slowly accumulating effects of continuing or intermittent exposure to relatively weak radiation. This sort of exposure may leave you yourself in good health and, if you have passed the age for reproduction, without discernible effect, although a little more might induce pernicious anemia or cancer; but if parenthood lies before you then pray for your children and your children's children. They may need it or, perhaps much better, should not be born. The effects of radiation accumulate in the reproductive cells of either sex, with sterility as the least unfortunate outcome. For irradiated reproductive cells, whether actually eggs or sperm or the parental tissue from which they grow, too often give rise to organisms which are definitely abnormal. Even those spontaneous changes which tend to occur from time to time among reproductive cells in any animal or plant are most likely to be disadvantageous, and all biological experimentation of the last half century shows that radiation of any sort makes matters worse. Pulling atoms apart to see how we can use the pieces may be an exciting human past-time, but the odds and ends that we are likely to leave around can so get into our own system and that of every other living thing, plant or animal, beautiful or grotesque, meek or mighty, that all we bequeath to the future may suffer from reproductive radiation rot. For we are playing with the fundamental mechanism of evolution without knowing what it is we do. In the end I believe the earth would recover from our tampering, but in the process of doing so it would have changed in ways we cannot foresee and too much is at stake to go forward blindly.

Evolution is the progressive change that populations of animals undergo in the course of time as the generations flicker by. And progressive does not necessarily mean better and better. It may only mean bigger and bigger and finally land the beasts in a quagmire as it did the mammoths when the permafrost melted beneath their feet, or it could mean more and more restricted to a peculiar diet such as ants or eucalyptus leaves, gambling all upon a single throw of the environmental dice. Or as in man it can mean increasing intelligence, plasticity and diversity—which accounts for our past and our present and gives us hope for the future if only we can keep the machinery clean and refrain from tinkering before we know how to operate it and before we know what we are supposed to produce.

To a great extent it is a question of genes, those units of heredity that all living cells contain. If genes in the reproductive cells are damaged or lost the product of development will be abortive or a monster or unfortunate in some vital respect and it is no accident I think that reproductive cells are to a great extent inviolate—although atomic radiation can reach them as readily as it can other tissues.

When you and I began our individual existence we consisted of a fertilized egg resulting from the fusion of an egg produced by our mother and a sperm furnished by our father. Each such cell contains thousands of genes all distinctively different, and each contains the same or similar set, which is characteristic of the human species. The combined cell which is the beginning of every individual existence consequently contains two sets of genes, perhaps twenty thousand in each, like two enormous packs of playing cards. Only each matched pair from the two sets are in most instances not exactly alike, as though one card had been marked and the other not. When the time comes to manufacture eggs and sperms for the next generation the double set of genes in each cell concerned is reduced to a single set, but without any consideration of whether a particular gene in a set came originally from one parent or the other. Single sets are produced once again with every kind of gene included, but in each set some, so to speak, will be marked and others not. This is important. It means that the chances of two eggs or two sperms even of the same parentage, ever being identical are so slim as to be virtually non-existent, and the chances of two fertilized eggs, being exactly alike are even less. No two children, except identical twins which come from a splitting of a single egg, can ever be the same, and when you consider that there are more than two billion people each with about twenty thousand pairs of genes in their reproductive cells, the total genetic pool in the human stock is therefore astronomical. This is the storehouse accumulated from the past and from which our genetic future will come. From the continual reshuffling from generation to generation during several hundred thousand years contemporary man evolved from the thicker skulled and smaller brained humans who struggled for existence far back in the ice age. And by similar reshufflings in the future this or that quality may become more pronounced. So our successors may turn out to be even larger brained and thinner skulled, with consequences I will speak of in a while, should we continue in the direction we have been moving.

Meanwhile, for the present, our essential nature is such that with so few exceptions as make no matter all men are different and the cult of conformity and uniformity fits us ill. We differ in height, in bodily type and facial characteristics, in shape of head and tendency to baldness, in color of eyes, hair and skin, in resistance to diseases, to heat and cold. We differ in all of these and in many other ways even within a so-called race. Yet we can all interbreed, within the races and between the races —even an Eskimo with a Hottentot under certain circumstances. We are all of one species and the more obvious regional differences come solely from long periods of continental segregation in the past. But all types can mix with biological if not sociological impunity, as you can see wherever Asia, Africa and Europe or any two of them come together—all are blended mixtures, without loss of comeliness, intelligence or health. In fact most of the segregated brands can stand improvement irrespective of numerical or self-regarding status. And whether we care for it or not the essential mixing is already too far gone to be halted. Genes which may have been distinctive of western European stock are diffusing through the population of Japan as the result of an army of occupation; oriental genes are pervading North America as Chinese and Japanese strains become incorporated. In the course of centuries the North American negro may disappear as the two-way flux of genes continue, when the dominant population will have shifted toward a light brunette, and the few thousand black people who may remain are likely to have straight hair, narrow noses and thin lips. South and Central America are already far along this road. I am as certain as I am of anything that the more outstanding regional distinctions between sections of mankind will fade away—isolation produced them and loss of isolation will obliterate them. In this sense we will be a mongrel race, but every so-called race that now exists is as mongrel as they come, for no matter how hard we try to believe our own particular ancestry is pure and undefiled, we all go back to a wild and woolly mixture of barbarian races and had better be glad of it. In this limited prospect the final state of man is better than the first and we can see something of it in the peoples south of the Himalayas where the Indo-Europeans from the northwest and the mongolians from the northeast have blended with mixtures of more primitive types, both australoid and negroid. The general outcome is warm or even dark colored, handsome and richly endowed with human quality. Perhaps when a stranger no longer looks strange, and can speak without being misunderstood, the ties of kinship may bind us closer.

Yet this sort of blending is far from uniformity. The differences between man and man, as distinct from those now separating men and men, will persist and if anything increase. It is the variety which is the spice of life, for I cannot conceive anything much more depressing than a world that was a repetition of myself, two billion times. If you saw your image on every face and knew the thought within was the same as yours —it would be a more exquisite hell than any I have heard of. The geographic differences have only a nuisance value now that mankind is on the move, but the basic individual differences have always existed and always will. Every human being who has ever lived, is here now or ever shall be is unique. The chances are overwhelmingly against the possibility that someone exactly the same as you will ever again exist in the universe, let alone on this planet at this particular time. And what is unique is always irreplaceable, for substitutes are something else, and herein lies our personal glory so long as we do nothing to dim it.

No man, woman or child is normal. The normal human is a fiction, a mathematically imaginary being compounded of the many and divided by a number. It is useful of course to have a standard of expectation, so that if you blow your horn at a pedestrian starting to cross the street you will be pretty sure he will jump back on the curb, although there are alternative responses. This is possible because we are all basically alike up to a point; yet beyond this point we differ—I would in fact define mankind as a brotherhood of heretics, with every one designed for a heresy of his own. Unfortunately we tend to behave towards our fellow beings as though we were anything but brothers and as though we were all supposed to be alike, supposed to react in the same way to any given circumstances, to hold the same thoughts about God and the universe and what is good to eat. Anyone who disagrees with you on seemingly important issues must be a fool or a knave or a sinner, and persecution for divergent beliefs has stained human history through and through. It is time we took stock.

The self-evidence that all men are created equal is a spiritual truth rather than a social or a biological fact—an affirmation that all men ought to have an equal chance, not that they have or that they are all equally well equipped by nature. The rights of man are not rights that any man possesses—they are claims, and at the root is the implicit belief that all seeds should sprout and grow and flower and bring forth fruit, that none should lie fallow or grow in stunted form; it is the belief in the sacredness of life in Hindu religion and in Schweitzer's philosophy of reverence for life and is the antithesis of the concept of nature red in tooth and claw where the only right is might.

Human rights are those that mankind recognises and instinctively desires, for being born neither free of our biological and social environment or of our sustaining organismal needs, nor equal in natural qualities and potentialities, no one of us has more or less right to life than any other creature. We have the power of decision, by virtue of our might, whether this kind of life or that kind of life shall survive and in what quantity. We are in fact uncomfortably like the captain of a ship in distress whose life boats will hold only a part of the living cargo—who shall be saved and who shall perish? We cannot avoid the responsibility under the circumstances for we have already assumed command, but the burden is heavy and we need all the wisdom we can get, not to mention humility and compassion.

In any human family you take it for granted that human personalities will flourish insofar as harmony, affection, and mutual understanding play their part, that minds will grow to the extent that thought is stimulated, and that the condition of both bodies and souls depends on how large the family is in relation to its means of support. What is true of the family unit holds for humanity as a whole. Both the harmony that comes from a sense of community and of common origin, and the recognition and appreciation of human differences are essential for well being, so long as physical health is assured. But we must accept the differences and make the most of them, rather than gloss them over or pretend they are not there, or what is worse to try to rub them off in an effort to transform a group of cooperative human individuals into a social herd governed by a faceless collectivism—where the ideals of security, conformity and social acceptance stifle the individual's inborn instinct to grow and transcend himself as a person.

Human beings vary in every quality of the mind and spirit as well as in physique and appearances, physiology and longevity. We differ in almost everything we can think of—in sense of taste and smell, reaction to color and sound, in our ways of doing things, in all our likes and dislikes, in our allergies and susceptibilities, in femininity or masculinity. Individualism is a greater attribute of the human species than of any other kind of living organism and much of the hate so rampant in human relations stems from this essential human diversity and our failure to accept and understand it. As Emerson said—the only sin we never forgive in each other is difference of opinion. Yet how can any two opinions be exactly alike when no two minds are ever the same? Rather than force our children along the lines of standardized sociability, fostering the illusion that they are supposed to be a uniform product of a human assembly line, we should be teaching them that the juvenile passion to be average, normal and secure is a retreat from life. That life is adventure, novelty, and above all the discovery of self, that all the springs of worthwhile action have come from individual minds, not from group assemblies, and that talent buried is talent lost—that each and every human being has qualities and capacities in combination that are all his own.

There is no such thing as mature mind or pure intelligence or creative art—these are abstractions which have their use—but there are and have been individuals with mature minds, with high intelligence of this or that kind, and with whatever leads to creative action. The cult of the common man is an insult and a degradation when no man is common except as circumstances make him so, and in an age when technological routine has replaced the crafts and free time is usurped by vicarious living the individual needs all the help he can get to find and be himself. He needs to know, and to know as a child that he is the only one of his kind and that his companions are each different in ways of their own. He needs to know that whether his gifts are large or small they are his own, that he sees the world around him in a somewhat different way than has ever been seen before. And he needs to know that when all minds are uncommon the most uncommon may have by far the most to tell. He needs to know for instance that Hamlet and the Taj Mahal were individual creations unmatched and never to be repeated; that all that we admire most in ancient Egyptian architecture and sculpture burst suddenly into being as the creation or inspiration of a single uncommon mind, that of the priest Imhotep of the 3rd dynasty who was later made a god. And he should know that the greater the minds the greater the differences.

The special qualities of the mind are related to the particular nature of the brain. Brains vary in size and there is a greater chance for unusual development in a large brain than in a small one, although the fueling system is important and so is the extent to which the brain is used. Yet we all have brains of an astonishing size and complexity, and even when total volumes are the same the component parts may vary greatly from one brain to the next. This brain may have relatively large and complex regions associated with visual memory, that one may be no more than average in this respect but the regions concerned with the storage of sound may be unusually well-developed, while in another the regions farther forward associated with the sense of dynamic space and present and future action may be comparatively outstanding, or the whole may be more or less subjected to the flooding emotions of deeper centers. Everything is in some sort of balance but the balance is made by different forms of weighting and no two are identical. And as the brain has grown the differences between one and another are magnified accordingly. When the visual regions reach their peak a Michaelangelo can arise creating in shape and color and solid form; when vision combines with the sense and memory of dynamic action you get Leonardo da Vinci—not only a painter but an inventor who might have set the world in motion had he lived a little later; but when the recording mechanisms for sound overbalance the rest, and opportunity in time and instruments are present, a Beethoven weaves sound into musical patterns that lift the soul of man. These are uncommon giants I fully realise but they are giants who grew out of the so-called common stock of a multitude of uncommon individuals of lesser stature. And they stand as symbols in more ways than one.

They stand as symbols of the creative individuality of human beings, as symbols of the manifold facets of sense and mind, and as symbols of beauty. In their very being, in the joy and labor and process of creation, and in their bequest to the human world about them and to come they challenge mankind to make a choice, to determine what its values are and to foster them. Above all they show us a path which lies ahead, if only we can see our way clear to take it, for I doubt if a rampaging, voracious multibillion human herd can squeeze along it. We are faced with the questions of quantity and quality, which each one of us can answer only for himself.

20

PERSONAL EQUATION

As an individual I want to see myself clearly for what I am. What am I as a human being and what kind of individual am I? What concerns me and what does not, and why? These are questions of universal application in spite of such peculiar uniqueness that I myself possess, but they are personal also in a more intimate sense. I am aware of being alive and awake to the pouring in of the universe through my senses, aware of personal continuity in spite of continual change, aware that I had a beginning and will have an individual end. I am aware of myself, sometimes uncomfortably so, and with some effort I can also see myself almost as though I was on the outside looking in. In other words, as a symbol of humanity I can learn more from me than I can from you.

I know something of my limitations as well as my capacities. I know that my mind is strongly visual and that I can think in terms of visual images almost without the use of words, but my memory for music and language and all things heard is practically nil, and I am forced to operate in the only way I can. The mathematical approach to the universe and the physics of the atom are virtual mysteries—while curved space that must not be visualized is outside my comprehension, though I accept it as something that others can conceive even though I cannot. This is important because by extension I become aware that all minds are limited no matter how well they may perform in one way or another. And there is a haunting thought that the universe or reality which we are trying to comprehend is not only queerer than we think, it is queerer than we can think. At times you get the feeling of being trapped within the rigid walls of your own skull, a prisoner whose patterns of thought are set both by the speech we have recently acquired and by the long interminable series of circumstances that have brought us to where we are. Whether we would prefer to overlook it or not, our ancestry has been by way of the ape and our brain has been molded by the demands put upon it in the course of the last fifty million years—human mentality has grown from ape mentality and the constraints are still with us to a frustrating degree. We may be the most elegant ape that ever walked, but the simian past has set limits to the way we can see, although it has given us a view of the stars. And it is vital I think to recognise not only that there are limits to the kind of thinking we can do and to how much we can comprehend, but to recognise a mental wall when we come up against one, particularly if we assume that one of our greatest needs, if not the greatest, is to understand the nature of the universe in which we find ourselves to be playing a part.

If we, like all other living things, have grown out of the earth itself, we have as much need to see and find ourselves within the whole scheme of things as to become immersed in our own particular nature without reference to the rest. We do not exist in isolation, nor as a creator's afterthought designed to exploit what went before, but as a part of an evolving universe, perhaps as vital a part as any. In this light we ourselves, in what we do and think and feel, indicate the nature of the whole to a profound degree. What then are the drives that keep us in motion?

There are the drives connected with hunger, safety, mating and comfort which we share with all creatures to a great extent. They relate to the general nature of animate organisms and take us too far afield. I am more concerned with what is distinctively human since so much of human mind and spirit is a newly emergent quality on this planet. For this is the signpost to the future, not our capacity to outbreed and outconsume the rest of creation—for unless quality concerns us first and last and quantity hardly at all, I have nothing to say and not much more desire to be. Yet the compulsion to speak continues and is itself a fact to be considered.

I can speak as a man with a long personal experience as an individual and as a member of a family. I can speak as an educator since that is my livelihood. And I can speak as some sort of scientist since such is my vocation, and as such I believe I can see more clearly than I can in other ways. Yet what constitutes a scientist is no longer simple to answer, although it used to be; now the question is as if I had asked whether you are religious—if you replied without first taking thought, whatever your answer, I would wonder if you knew.

Science in recent times has enlarged so that we now tend to think of it in capital letters. It has become the giant symbol of man's mastery of the forces and resources of nature which brings with it a sense of achievement and power which most of contemporary humanity feels it shares whether it has directly contributed or not. A good example may be useful: at one of the annual occasions when thousands of scientists meet to hear the latest news on the scientific front a team of workers issued a joint statement that they had for the first time harnessed sunlight to create sugar and starch out of water and carbon dioxide in the absence of green plants. It was proclaimed without fanfare but it was reported elsewhere as heralding a 'sun civilization' of unlimited abundance, as a golden age of plenty, and the general feeling was that of a prominent automotive scientist-engineer that the human race must some day become independent of plant life and that within the next fifty years man will liberate himself from the tyranny of green growing things.

Note four things: the discovery was the work of a group co-operating to form a team, the result is a high technical achievement of perhaps revolutionary potentiality, it has been seized upon by other minds as knowledge which can be converted into power, and the power is to be used to maintain human populations presumably far in excess of what the earth's green cover can sustain. The outcome so far as I can see would be a population so universally dense—the ambiguity is justified— that there would virtually be sitting room only with no means of avoiding the surrounding human growth, and we would be supplied with an ever present source of unappetizing self-manufactured nourishment. We might as well be cabbages and be done with it. Even the barnacle lost its head when it settled on a rock and kicked food into its mouth with its feet. This is not the way to wisdom.

Yet it is science by popular acclamation and individually I suppose each member of the team in question would rank as a scientist both by training and attitudes. But it is science of a certain kind which is primarily the technological development of basic ideas already established. The activity involved, both at its conceptual and technical level, is exciting and enjoyable, but the excitement is that which comes from any intense activity of the mind when free from anxiety—the kind you see or feel at any time your mind is highly stimulated. Yet it is technological or applied science, not the fountainhead itself, and is essentially the same as the development of the atomic bombs and atomic energy from what was already known of atomic constitution. In both cases a group of scientists collaborated to exploit certain well-established ideas about the chemical and physical nature of matter to manufacture something that could be put to human use. The mental process most involved is conscious reasoning, and close reasoning combined with technical ingenuity has produced a partial model of the sun in the one case and of photosynthesis in the other. In a somewhat different and subtler form the creations are new and powerful machines which imitate nature, rather than significantly new insights. All the fundamental understanding for the making of atomic bombs was public scientific knowledge long before a bomb was thought of. And knowledge of that kind can never be kept secret for long, even if there is foresight enough to see the need, since secrets of nature are divulged by nature and not by man. In the words of Robert Oppenheimer—'there aren't any secrets about the world of nature. There are only secrets about the thoughts and intentions of men. Sometimes they are secret because a man doesn't like to know what he is up to if he can avoid it.'

Nature may seem to be secretive but that is an indication of the limitations of quality and general degree of development of the human brain. And under certain circumstances nature speaks freely to those who would listen—only her language is hard to comprehend. The fountainhead is nature herself, the same fountain which feeds religion and art as well as science, for at their source the three streams run together. But man as a communicant must approach her in a certain way and in a certain mood. It is a spirit which is incompatible with the drive for mastery, and as a rule the approach must be made alone.

I speak now for the solitary scientist, solitary in the sense of working more or less alone and free to follow where fancy beckons, for those individual human beings who are not in harness with a team the direction of which is firmly set, who are not yet captivated by scientific apparatus that must be kept in operation and only capable of answering questions put in terms the apparatus can understand. I suppose there are conditions even within modern scientific laboratories where the unfettered approach is still possible, but I am sure they become progressively hard to find as more and more refined and elaborate and expensive equipment comes to stand between human senses and the natural world. Moreover time and again you hear statements that the scope of human knowledge is now so vast that no single mind can possibly encompass it. I do not doubt it, but the situation is unfortunate for I do not believe you can put a number of human minds together in the same room and get anything better than the best of them. Team work is fine when there is a common understanding of the task in hand, whether it is to make a bomb or climb a mountain, but it has no place in creating a symphony or in comprehending something that has never been sensed before. The great creations and the great comprehensions, where the monumentally obvious is seen for the first time, are always the products or experiences of individual minds operating alone, free from the intrusions and distractions of other human voices.

The reason I think is clear. It is also vital to our well-being that we take it to heart as well as understand it, for it cuts deep into the soul. When men come together to promote a cause or to pool knowledge and understanding, they are limited in what they can bring and what they can take away by their means of communication, in other words their common language, which may be in various forms, scientific and otherwise. Anything that cannot be consciously formulated cannot be communicated and therefore remains within the mind that experienced it, which is why mystics are so hard to understand —their experience is beyond the capacity of speech.

I can only speak with certainty for myself but I am sure that apart from some special talent and some particular limitations I am typical of my species. I have perhaps had more time than most to do what pleases me and to consider why I do whatever it is I do. Teaching for instance is the basis for my employment and it brings its rewards in other ways as well, but I am left with control over much of my time and am under no definite pressure to carry on any particular kind of scientific work or in fact to do any at all. Yet these are just the conditions most nourishing to the scientific spirit, which is fundamentally contemplative, just as they would be to any other phase of the human spirit whether it be humanistic, artistic or religious. The kind of understanding I have in mind comes from insight, and insight cannot be forced. The insight which leads to new ways of looking at things is a product of the whole mind and not merely the conscious processes of reason or even imagination. There is more than dreams in the dim subconscious and I think it is a common experience, far more general than the scientific one, that more problems are solved and more understanding is reached between midnight and morning when the mind is said to be asleep than at other times. Without conscious thought the answers seem to rise unsought to the surface, so long as full attention has been given to them before. Joan of Arc heard her voices tell her what should be done for the sake of France and she believed them for they made sense—but like all such intimations, the reasons or proofs have to be found consciously *after* understanding has already arrived. Inspiration comes unexpectedly during the night or at some other time of quietness—not necessarily during silence but when it is possible to listen to the whispering inward voice. Then like a flooding illuminating light, order or meaning permeates previously disordered or tangled information and something new becomes part of the human world.

The important fact is this, that unless the mind stops thinking altogether, which is the commonest tragedy that befalls the mind, it thinks unceasingly about what the senses feed it, although we are only partly conscious of what is going on. We can control the process only by controlling what is fed into the mind, how fast it goes in, and how much time is allowed for the loom to weave its tapestry. When the material of what is woven comes direct from nature we assume that the pattern produced resembles reality, at least in part. It is an act of faith but it is one upon which all science and human action generally is based. And to a great extent such science is a form of recognition, the kind of understanding or insight which comes from close but unforced association with natural phenomena such as the growth of a flower or a child or a thought.

Science of this sort, which is like awareness and is distinct from putting things together to see what happens, began in Mesopotamia in towns or cities older than Ur itself, before 3000 B.C.; and from the beginning writing, accountancy, astrology and religion are intertwined. They all express the action of the discriminating mind busy classifying and arranging the apparent chaos of creation into categories of order. Most of it was related to the needs of farming and administration of the evolving state, but this was merely the drive that supplied motive and directed attention. The whole multiple activity itself seems to be the clear, outstanding, emergent quality of mind—of mind at least wrestling with the task of recreating the universe within it itself.

Recognition of the regularity and uniformity in the rise of the sun and the moon, in the change of seasons, and in the movements of the planets, was one of the first great experiences of mankind; and in the earliest systems of Mesopotamian or Babylonian astrology, mathematical and mythical language interpenetrate one another in a curious way. Yet Babylonian astronomers introduced the distinction between the different star groups and devised the twelvefold division of the Zodiac.

It was a recognition of external order which sank into the human mind, and emerged imperceptibly into consciousness, and the science I am most concerned with is essentially this process of understanding. Whether it has practical value is beside the point, except that the mind tends to go to sleep unless stimulating fires of some sort are kept alight within. Pythagoras in the sixth century B.C. extended the vision in the same general way when he realised that the pitch of sound depended on the length of vibrating chords—a startling enough discovery by itself and a perfect example of that dawning realisation which cannot be forced by reason, but also one which set the whole future orientation of philosophical and mathematical thought in the western world and led directly to the Copernican concept of the universe which is now our own. The construction of the periodic table of the elements and an understanding of the language of spectra in our own scientific age are discoveries of the same kind. So was Darwin's theory of evolution. In every case the process is one which I can describe only by analogy, like seeing with the mind rather than with the eye, and seeing with the whole mind and not only with that part in which consciousness and the powers of reason lie. It leads not to action but to understanding. Unfortunately understanding is also the tree of knowledge, which is generally best left alone. When we pluck its fruits we have to take the consequences.

It is this approach to the world and the universe around us which has much in common with both religion and art and has the same roots in the human spirit. All three bring man into direct communication with reality, but usually in such a way that the language of common speech breaks down when the need for communication arises. Hence mysticism and abstract art, mathematical symbolism and music. Yet above all else the reasoning and balancing powers of the intellect sit in judgment. For this is the strength of man, that he can attune

himself to nature—or whatever or whoever you want to call
it—and hear voices, and that having heard them he can judge
whether they are telling the truth or not. Although attune-
ment alone may become wild and uncontrolled imagination,
and reason by itself is a cold and deadly thing.

In our present state of western civilization we are increasingly inclined to employ the intellect alone, with everything
above the surface, much fermentation, and little time or opportunity for perspectives, contemplation or withdrawal. Most
of what now passes for science is done for a purpose and
supported by a grant which keeps the project rolling along a
track. Results are too important, particularly those of practical
significance, and mountains of information accumulate which
have never been digested; Masefield wrote that knowledge is
the fat that cloys men's minds, and to a great extent I am
sure this is true. It has become a sin to waste time.

My own inclination, opportunity, and experience has been
within the older and more leisurely form of science now no
longer fashionable, in the simple observation of living organisms with a minimum of interference. It has no practical value
that I can see. Nobody particularly cares whether I do it or
not except myself, and I care passionately. What I discover
brings no tangible reward and my sins of omission are not
penalized. I am fascinated by the moving microscopic pageant
of an egg developing into an organism and what I now realise
is that if you watch incessantly with all your attention, and do
not attempt to impose yourself, the organism eventually and
in its own way explains itself. You are wiser and richer for it,
but the approach must be made with a genuine humility and
with none of the conquering superman attitude. I know of
little that is more rewarding. But the time and effort involved
cannot be justified except on the grounds of pure enjoyment
and the satisfaction which comes from watching beauty and
bringing your mind to its fullest pitch of awareness. That is

its primary value, and it is personal. The full experience is mine alone, although to a great extent and with much effort I can communicate the essential meaning to others, which is an entirely different procedure of re-creation and is comparable to a musician laboriously writing out the score after he has already heard the music in his mind. That such as this can be done only for its own sake however I believe is the greatest justification it is possible to find, and to the extent that we depart from this motive I believe we prostitute our spirit. The two most obvious characteristics of nature, it is said, are loveliness and power, and when we concentrate upon power alone we do so at our peril.

Atomic physics has been prostituted in the mid-twentieth century just as chemistry was a century earlier, as the subsequent reactions of Alfred Nobel and our contemporary physicists testify. That is the danger which is always present. It is difficult to foresee the evil use to which understanding of the nature of matter, energy or even life can be put. In fact I believe such foresight is for the most part impossible to attain, nor can we remain human and put a stop to the fundamental activty of the human mind.

So far the study of embryos and other developing organisms has not been directed towards control but only understanding, and may it stay this way, for whereas a bird or a flower or even a worm can be breathtakingly beautiful in its finished form, the whole unfolding creative process whereby it grows into being from an egg is almost unbelievable though you see it happen before your eyes.

Yet even here there is a danger of subornation. Attempts are continually being made to raise embryos of mammals such as mice, rats or rabbits in artificial fluids outside the maternal body as so-called test-tube babies, mainly to see more of the processes involved than can be studied otherwise. It is a legitimate technique and is not essentially different in kind from what is done to the developing eggs of frogs and starfish—all just part of that curiosity that makes you want to take a watch or any other intricate mechanism apart to see what makes it go. But suppose the technique becomes perfected and applicable to human eggs and embryos—do you believe we would leave it well enough alone? I don't. I am sure that under some sort of imposing name we would attempt and possibly succeed in propagating human beings in glass or plastic containers in a fancy factory. It would be a tremendous technical achievement and the idea may appeal to men like that of sending rockets to the moon—something which brings that superior feeling but adds little to our understanding of either human beings, embryos, or the moon. To me the thought of test-tube babies when applied to man is appalling and I want no part of it either directly or inadvertently. Yet the dream exists among some of my professional colleagues, while those Russian biologists who have recently grafted the head of a small dog into the neck of a larger one to make a living two-headed atrocity I am sure would feel it was a goal worth striving for. With what result? At the best useless, and at the worst the capacity to manufacture even more dehumanized but intellectual monsters lusting for the reins of power than afflict us as it is. All that is human has grown within the family and we should cherish our birthright, not throw it away.

Yet such a project I believe would soon be self-defeating—too poor a model of the original design. But there is another possibility that is by no means fantastic. Among the more intriguing problems confronting embryologists is the nature of the chemical changes which occur at the surface of an egg at the moment of fertilization by a spermatozoan. Much is already known and I have little doubt that a reasonably full understanding will come before long. We are consequently likely to discover as much about the nature and peculiarities of sperm as about the process of fertilization itself, and inasmuch as in most animals including humans there are two types of sperm but only one type of egg, and the union of one type of sperm with the egg results in a male and the union of the other results in a female, we may readily stumble upon some simple chemical means of sex control, whereby the activity of one type of sperm is encouraged at the expense of the other. If the controlling agent became simple to make and universally accessible, which is a possibility we cannot discard, mankind thereafter would be in control of its sex ratio. Or would it? Only if the control lay in the hands of a master-minding politburo. Otherwise I feel sure that our continual efforts to maintain a balance would be like violently rocking the boat. There is such a general predilection for sons rather than daughters that males would immediately outnumber females possibly several to one—a difficult social problem to have to face—and unless the trend was immediately reversed the result could be a decimation of the human population through reduction in the numbers of the propagative sex. More likely the first overbalance would be so disturbing that the general tendency would be to swing strongly in the opposite direction and in one or two generations produce a superabundance of females—who might of course get control of the situation and evolve a matriarchal society with a small percentage of virile and high quality males produced primarily for stud purposes. Probably we would just keep on overshooting the mark from one side and the other indefinitely. In one form or another the knowledge and the power so gained would be something which we would thereafter have to live with just as we have to make the best of the fact that we now know how to produce atomic bombs. Only a catastrophic remedy as bad as the disease could destroy the knowledge itself and restore us to a relative state of innocence.

All of this raises a problem which is personal in the extreme. It concerns everyone of us, but I can see this particular case arising more clearly than I can others. There is no possibility that I myself will discover such a means of sex control or even contribute in a small way to making such a discovery. But my interests have been such that under somewhat different conditions and a little later in time I might well have done so. It would not be a discovery that would add much to our understanding of the fertilization process, which is why it is not being aimed at directly, but it is one that might easily come as a by-product of such understanding. Supposing I had discovered it, what would I do?

Much would depend upon my age and circumstances. There might be an opportunity to patent the discovery and make a fortune, as in the case of a wonder drug, and the temptation to do so might be overwhelming. Yet that would be actually of little importance except for my own peace of mind. If I was a young man I am sure I would in any case communicate my discovery to my colleagues as soon as possible and would receive acclaim, for it is an observed form of human behavior that research workers in general must communicate or burst, once they have made any kind of exciting discovery. The two satisfactions of indulging in idle curiosity and sharing the results go hand in hand and you cannot suppress the one without dampening the other, for the hardest thing any child can do is to keep a secret and a carefree scientist is at heart more child-like than most of his more acquisitive or less fortunate compatriots. This comparison is not meant invidiously but it is a fact that must be accepted. A state that wants a plentiful supply of secretive scientists is like a man who wants oranges to taste like lemons, he can have one or the other but not both inside the same rind. You can keep secrets of little real importance but you can't make great discoveries or reach profound understandings under conditions of secrecy, for the natural state of man is to see all, hear all and tell all. I know for myself that my urge to study the ways of simple organisms would die at once if I was convinced I could never speak or write about them to any one else—the sharing is all-important, at least in prospect.

There is another side to all of this. If I made a discovery such as the means of human sex control now I would suppress it. I would not trust any group of human beings, whether an elect committee or the medical fraternity or the state or humanity at large to make wise use of it, even if I had faith that there would be no deliberate exploitation to serve particular ends. The basic issue however is not whether mankind would or would not be competent to make good use of knowledge placed at its disposal but whether the collective state— whether limited or all-inclusive—has a natural right to all that its constituents can contribute, or even whether aggregated but unorganized humanity has such a right. Or whether the individual has the inherent right to withhold his experience from the common pool, as distinct from avoiding exploitation for his own benefit at the expense of others. I believe he has. Unless a man has sold or given his mind and soul to a corporation, a state or a cause, he remains primarily an individual responsible for every act and in some degree for its consequences. As such he becomes his own judge and jury, and there are few more severe. Moreover while the individual may not be able to choose the best course to take, society knows no better. As a rule however there is not much choice and the most potent knowledge is broadcast long before its use for evil can be foreseen.

Yet the spirit of science is akin to worship, for it is the effort of the mind to reach and enter into the wonder of the universe from the atom to the star and from life to thought. This is the heart of it. Some awareness of beauty, an implicit love of universal nature and joy in understanding are demanded for full satisfaction. The individual profits most I think because of this sense of self-fulfillment. And generally speaking the greatest insights come when they are sought for no ulterior motives and when self is completely submerged in what is contemplated. Without these attitudes the methods and techniques of science may still be used, particularly for reaching results of practical importance, but they are not the keys to the kingdom.

21

THE SHAPE OF WONDER

I FEEL somewhat like a sculptor who has found the right rock for the shaping of man and who has cut away a large amount of stone in search for the form within. Now with so little left, what manner of man do we find? And if it is a living form with a long life ahead, where lies its destiny?

To get an objective view of something you have been studying closely is never easy, especially when you yourself are involved in the object of study. It took a Dutchman in America to describe England as a little island off the coast of Holland, which is a viewpoint no Englishman could adopt. And now I have the same difficulty, for in describing man I describe myself and the objective and subjective outlooks become inseparable. In what follows therefore I speak for myself as an individual of a particular kind with certain inclinations, I speak as a man representative of our species looking at mankind as well as science and history permit, and I speak as a scientist concerned with the development and evolution of organisms and as such I shall try to show a way to the future. It is a hopeful way, which I believe we can travel if we take our time.

Time however is paramount. There is no indication that we have changed during the last ten thousand years, only that we have become more and more and busier and busier, like a swarming up-rooted colony of ants. To find men with appreciably thicker skulls and slightly smaller brains we have to go back ten times as far. Whatever happens in the future will be slow by any human yardstick and we have to adjust our individual feeling for time to the scale of that which brought us into being. When we assume that mankind or its transformed descendants will indefinitely continue to dominate this planet as in the past few millennia we are taking a longer view of the future than is generally recognized: not a few thousand years or even a million but in terms of the habitable earth itself, of the order of a thousand million years—time far beyond what the mind can grasp. Yet it is the view we must take if it is to mean anything at all, for we are planning for keeps or else we look forward to a time when we step aside. Either way we are caretakers for our successors whether they be our direct descendants or those of other creatures who have been less ambitious. And in any case we hold the present in trust and may one day be judged by the mark we leave upon the earth and its life.

It seems to me that we generally think of man and nature as if it were a natural division, although we have excuse enough considering the way our cities grow and how we devastate the land around. Yet the inescapable truth is that we are a part of nature, within nature, and only a recent innovation at that. Life had a very long and a very diversified history on this planet before we emerged and no one has guaranteed us our right to possession—we could be a passing whim of creation fading away as imperceptibly as we began, with no one to mourn us or to realise that we had ever been. And unless we had irrevocably poisoned the planet with radioactive waste during our incumbency the world would roll on around its sun without us, wonderfully rich and beautiful, incessantly evolving new forms of life on land and in the sea and in the air. Color and scent and sound would still be sensed by other creatures. Birds would still sing for joy, flowers would still grow in season, and other mammals might evolve a large though different sort of brain more consciously earthborn and earthbound than ours. Beauty would remain, to be sought and to be seen. Yet it would be a shame to falter and step aside when we have come so far; for if the fertility of a planet is life and the fruit of life is mind, then the human species becomes the first sign of real wakefulness in the solar system. And this I believe is our true meaning and significance.

We are a certain kind of animal. That to a great extent is fortuitous. We might have been very different in a structural way and still have become human in the ways that matter, although the accidents of our mammalian history have had much to do toward evolving our particular kind of mind. We have a body that calls for better use than sitting in a chair or for pushing pedals, and we have hands that are far superior as tools to any we have made, and they cry for skills to give them satisfaction. And inasmuch as body and mind can never be completely disassociated these things are important. The masculine prediliction for reaching mountain tops comes from the desire to exercise both aspects of the organism simultaneously.

The qualities of the mind however concern us more—and I am using the term to embrace all that we associate with spirit, soul, mind and brain; the distinctions are arbitrary and the collective whole is in any case too subject to the physiological whims of the body, for I have little doubt that we are each of us all of one piece. Yet the fact which has the greatest possible meaning is that we have reached a threshold. We had already attained it when our predecessors were painting pictures in the caves of Europe, but since then the nature of the threshold has become somewhat clearer.

Evolution has an emergent quality. When atoms combine to form molecules new properties emerge which are those of the new complex and not of the isolated components. When molecules combine among themselves, other qualities arise; and when the inconceivable molecular complexity we call protoplasm is formed, the new qualities or properties become those of life itself. Each progressive step brings forth a surprise, unforseeable when looking ahead but understandable when looking back. Mind emerges from living substance in consequence of a similar increase in bulk and complexity, a condition that all the more active animals have attained. And selfconscious mind comes into being as a mind with new emergent qualities when the human brain reached something like its present degree of expansion and elaborate refinement. We are now experiencing for better and for worse what these new qualities mean to us. Much of the mind's capacities have been essential to our survival, but many of the qualities I am sure would have been unpredictable. Large brains were favored I think for their greater capacity for memory and for powers of reason—their owners were more likely to live to reproductive maturity and generation by generation the drift toward larger brains continued. But other qualities which we are inclined to set apart as those of the soul or spirit were equally called forth by the successive advances. We have rather suddenly broken on to a higher plain of existence which was unforeseen, but now that we are here we can look back and see how it happened, and here and there among other creatures we can recognize a little of what we now possess in relative abundance. Yet the consciousness of self is as yet incomplete and the nature of the new kind of mind which we call man must be observed in that same contemplative and scientific spirit which we apply to other forms of nature. It is not easy, but the detached and objective regard is essential if we are to reach conclusions. Reason can then examine them and weigh them in the balance, and feeling can acknowledge the truth or warn that it is impure or incomplete.

What the mind does when a person is engrossed in finding sustenance or is working under direction or is in a semi-coma from too much food or from the lack of it is not significant. I am not concerned with the driven or the sleepy mind but with one that is fully alert and free to express itself, for the mind shows its true nature only when it is free to play, free to be itself as fully as possible, just as a child will climb a tree under conditions of vigorous health, mental relaxation and the presence of an arboreal paradise. Our true nature comes to the fore in those activities that give us the greatest joy when we are free from constraint or anxiety, and our true values appear in what, under other circumstances, we are prepared to live for and if necessary die for. The being which emerges may or may not be in the image of God, but at least he is new in this corner of the universe.

Through most of the past we have been slaves to our senses and to a great extent are captives still, although we are no longer bound by smell like the rest of our mammalian kin. We miss a lot but we gain a lot. We have developed touch to an astonishing degree, which allows creative urges their tangible expression. But above all we are indebted to eyes and ears and a sense of action, although our eyes and ears are not the best in the animal kingdom. Yet they are good enough and the amazing newness is of another kind.

We see, but we see more than the light and shadow and color recorded by the retina, more than meaningful forms and movements that mean life or death or sociability—we see a sunset or a rainbow or a flower and call it beauty. We see expression on a face and see radiance within—and call it beauty. We see unfolding growth in a child, in its mind and body, and call it beauty. I know of no other name to call it.

We hear, but the sounds take on meaning though they are but percussions in the air. The mind now weaves them into patterns of symbols that form channels of thought between mind and mind. Speech seems so natural and all pervasive that we forget its import and fail to realise the isolation and awkwardness of thought if sound had no significance. We pool our wisdom in gaseous waves and think nothing of it. Yet sound is beaten into other patterns which cannot be traced to thought. Beaten into rhythms and molded into tones we get a sense of movement, cycles, harmony, and time itself, in forms which speak directly to the spirit and the emotions leaving intelligence untouched. It conveys feeling and loveliness. We call it music, yet what else can it be but beauty?

I know beauty but I do not know what it means. Keats said that beauty is truth and so did the Greeks, although the one was concerned with loveliness and the others mainly with intellect. I do know that whatever beauty is, whether it is the kind that is woven within the mind itself or is perceived without, on this earth only the human mind can sense it. We can shut it out or kill it, and to that extent we die ourselves, but it is every man's birthright and children recognise it instinctively in its simpler forms. And inasmuch as we ourselves, in body, brain or mind, are as integral a part of the universe as any star, it makes little difference whether we say beauty lies only in the mind of the beholder or otherwise. We, each of us, you and I, exhibit more of the true nature of this universe than any dead Saturn or Jupiter, and if beauty is built in to our minds and has nowhere else to live, it still remains beauty and we have even greater reason to cherish it. Yet I do not think this is the case. I believe that somehow, as our brains have grown beyond a certain complexity and size, beauty emerged both as perception and as creation. We know it when we meet it and we create it when we can. And we know it in many forms and not only in sublimited senses—we know it when love becomes selfless and solicitude becomes compassion. We see it in moral stature and in hope and courage. We see it wherever the transcending quality of growth is clear and unmistakable, knowing that only in such growth do we find our own individual happiness.

When you speak of divinity the divine flies out the window, someone said. And I feel it is much the same with beauty and love. We can express them with words but cannot define them—we can only say that this and this are included but that is not, and wordlessly we all recognise the truth of it. Speech is limited, no matter what the language, and here I think we are not unlike a dog who feels intensely the bonds of loyalty and devotion but cannot speak. For in our hearts we understand more than we can possibly talk about.

We know that quality counts far above quantity. We cannot prove it but we can live by it. We know that once a life has begun to grow it should develop to its utmost, and that a flower nipped in the bud or a child dead is wrong. We know that when an animal or a plant becomes extinct, whether lovely or grotesque or simply different, the earth is poorer. We know loss when we destroy beauty for the sake of power or water. We know that when we kill, whatever the provocation or incentive, whether man or beast, harm has been done to more than flesh and blood. Or if we do not then we fall short of being human, and sooner or later we usually know this too. To destroy or repress the growth of body or spirit or recognisable beauty in any of its manifestations is evil. I believe it is the only evil that we know—that instinctively we acknowledge the supreme values of the emergent quality we sense within us and recognise without in all of nature, and insofar as we realise it and hinder its expression we feel guilty of sin, the only sin there is. Conscience was born when this brain of ours reached its present dimensions, and it raises an intriguing question: If our brain should grow larger and better with a corresponding development of mind, will we suffer greater remorse or will we stop sinning against the light? The latter seems to make more sense.

What of reason? It is not ours alone although we have carried it to new heights. In some degree we cannot deny it to cats and dogs and apes who to a certain extent can comprehend a puzzling situation or even put one and two together. Intelligence has had a gradual evolving throughout our arboreal and post-arboreal past, and all that we can be reasonably sure of is that it has grown steadily as the brain has expanded. Yet the conscious powers of mind include capacities which were uncalled for and unpurchased—gifts from the gods which are dangerous to hold.

It is easier to say what thought does than what thought is; attempts to explain it are really the mind turning in upon itself, a self consciousness which is phenomenal to say the least. Thought in action is essentially a process of understanding, of seeing some sort of complex whole in terms of actual or symbolic images, of separating one apparent component from another, of conceiving connections, and foreseeing how a change in a part affects the rest. This is no more than an indication, for I have no wish to become involved here in a discussion which from the nature of its subject may have no end. Yet we are all aware that the mind leaps toward an understanding as well as it can whenever we ourselves are involved in a situation; and whether it is a traffic accident, a shortage of money, a declaration of war, or your place in the scheme of things, the activity is mainly one visual imagery immersed in time and movement. Even the mind of a chimpanzee appears to work along these lines, although in a much more rudimentary way, and this resemblance in kind which we have with the ape is both our strength and limitation. Quite apart from differences in intensity and range of intelligence we are far more sightminded than a dog or any other mammal in which the sense of smell contributes so much information, yet even in a dog I doubt whether odors in general operate in a different manner than they do through our own abortive sense. Sound under certain conditions of pattern and change can induce joy or sadness, or even excitement—responses which are primarily emotional but not of the intellect; while sounds in the form of words are symbols of things, qualities and actions and enter thought only insofar as they are evocative or selective—unless my own mind is so steeped in vision that it is not typical. In any case it is difficult if not impossible to imagine any quality that has no basis in your own experience.

When we are left alone and are not thinking of personal relationships or where the next meal is coming from our thoughts wander into space and time, weave patterns out of the passing present and the life of yesterday, and become both meditative and speculative. Even when idling along, without incentive except for pleasure in being alive, the process is essentially a creating of order out of a chaos of immediate and remembered sensory impressions, a persistent and almost effortless process of bringing together a sequence of different facts and happenings from the well of memory. Unless the mind is driven by urgency in a particular direction something akin to reverie goes on incessantly, even in sleep in a disorderly way. Such is the loom on which the tapestries of light are woven, though they are shot through with emotion and vibrate to sound. Yet deep within it you feel there is someone, which is you, who mixes the colors as they feed in and, more significantly, scans the results for meaning and in the rather wistful hope of finding his own image.

Freedom begins here. The freedom to think untrammeled and to speak accordingly, the freedom for thought to soar if possible, and the freedom of the mind to be for the sake of being, in the sense that a thing of beauty is a joy forever and needs no other sanction. And joy comes to the mind when it is most fully aware of beauty in its broadest and deepest sense, and when thought for the sake of thinking is exercised most strongly. There is always satisfaction in doing what you are best designed to do, whether it is climbing a mountain, painting a picture, or solving a problem; and if the achievement is considerable there is always a certain amount of pain—the labor pains that accompany every birth—for only then do you know that you yourself are fully and consciously alive. For the finest performance of the mind a man should work for no reason except that which is the very life within him, for an element of slavery creeps in when the will, whether your own or someone else's, drives the mind to work for other motives. The performance may still be good but it is not so freely given and the difference can be noted. A man may enter science for the sake of benefiting humanity—an unselfish and noble purpose—but unless he becomes completely seduced he will serve both to the satisfaction of neither. You cannot travel freely along a predetermined path, for where freedom lies there is no path. And pure science, like pure art, whether of painting, poetry or music, is self directed and fancy free, and is a creation of individual minds working alone except for sources of inspiration.

I am not here concerned with moral obligations or with any obligation except that of the human spirit to express and recognise itself. You cannot study the course of a homing bird if you keep it captive, nor can you see what evident joy there is in flight if flight is not free. And it is only when the mind is keyed to a high pitch, is directed by intuition controlled by reason, and free of all external restraint, can you see the course it follows and feel its drive toward the heavens. Then it is that science, art, history and religion all seem to converge into a single whole, each portraying a facet with a color of its own yet each reflecting something of the rest. Science, with which I am more intimately involved, is concerned no less than religion and art with truth and beauty, and in some ways is more illuminating since it itself is better understood.

Science at this level, where it is conducted for no rewards and for no useful purpose, is enlightening. It is based on faith, though a faith that is instinctive and not based on any dogma. It is faith that the universe we construct from the impressions of our senses has some correspondence in reality, that we are part of nature and sensible to it. It is faith that by opening the windows of intuition and bringing all the power of reason to bear we can understand the nature of reality to a considerable extent. And it is faith that there is an all-pervading unity throughout all of nature and the universe as a whole, that it all has coherent meaning and is all of one piece including the scientist who attempts to discover and understand it. There is room for neither God nor space outside it, neither broken rules, nor interference, but the whole is both the song of creation and the singer himself—without beginning and without end.

All that can be seen or heard or felt or smelled, directly or indirectly, is brought to the scientist's loom, and only insofar as our senses themselves are limited is the raw material selected or restricted. Much of it brings sheer delight for itself alone. More of it runs into memory to be drawn upon as whim suggests. Most of it is continually resorted and matched for inspiration and woven into one frabic after another. Intuition brings them to the surface where reason is impelled to wrestle with all its might to conceive order in what lies before it. And each discovery is charged with joy as in the creation of a work of art. New hypotheses come into being most freely when intense effort raises discursive reasoning to a level where it unites with emotion. Whitehead in fact suggested that energy, mind and emotion are simply three aspects of one and the same fundamental stuff of the universe which we abstract separately for our own mental convenience It may be so, for our categories of order and being are at least as much within our minds as without.

Scientific procedure is essentially the persistent testing of hypotheses, which represent order, against fresh or recalled observations, and any correspondence seen is taken as a symptom of the truth though not the truth itself and certainly not the whole truth. And step by step the search for correspondence goes deeper and wider and wider. Yet whenever the pool of light spreads into the edge of gloom there has always been a great and fatiguing effort of rational thought controlled and disciplined by emotion. Without the sustaining faith in the unity of all things I doubt whether such efforts would be maintained, and the strength of it I believe is simply the intuitive recognition of the universal beauty which is the quality of harmony or oneness. It is this unity that is slowly being brought before the gaze of consciousness when we construct or reconstruct the whirling complexities of atoms and stars and the systems of molecules and organisms.

It is the nature of our language that when we see, or think we see, a universal plan that we immediately speak of a planner or creator, either as one who conceived it all and set it in motion or as one everpresent and in superimposed and potentially capricious control. The distinction is of our own making and is by no means a necessary one. It tells us more about the way we are inclined to think than it does about ultimate nature, and to conceive a god-like operator forever pulling the strings of his puppets is no compliment either to what is human or divine. We are plagued with a creeping egoistic anthropocentric standpoint that is continually giving us a biased view. It is natural enough but indicates immaturity if not actual infancy of outlook.

Yet the instinct to look for a planner in the planned may be more significant than the idea itself. If we accept the Greek saying that man is the measure of all things, then the craving in man for intelligibility, uniformity and simplicity wherever he looks means that the intellect is seeking in the universe that which conforms most closely to its own nature—that we do not walk upon an alien earth and that something in the universe corresponds to human intelligence. But we do not have to put it outside the universe and give it separate existence, whether we call it God or the creative principle, for we are merely on the threshold of discovery and should not jump to conclusions concerning the nature of reality from our first flickering glimpse of it. As we emerge into the light— if we do—we will not be disappointed or disillusioned by its radiance. The mystics of all religions and all ages confirm this, for they have stepped a little farther over the threshold than the rest of us and the quality of their experience appears to be overwhelming—an experience which combines thought and feeling in an indivisible whole and brings the individual mind seemingly into closer union with the divine essence or ultimate reality. The difficulty is that whatever the experience may signify it seems to be translated within the mind into terms of sensory impressions and deep emotion—there is no other medium for it. And while the fact of the mystic's experience is evident to others and is sometimes acknowledged with shattering repercussions, the nature of the experience, except for the mystic himself or, just as likely, herself, remains wrapped up in a language incapable of conveying its meaning. Language is meant only for communication of shared experience, not for reports from the frontier of the human spirit. Even William Blake with all his genius for poetic and graphic expression and his exaltation of imagination and intellect is only partly understood.

Yet fundamentally the extremely personal approach of the mystic to what he may call Nature, God, the Divine, or simply the universe, is shared in some degree by most scientists who are concerned solely with the nature of things. For the greatest scientific insights, which have survived the most rigorous scrutiny, have come when the mind has virtually been one with what it contemplates, when self as a person or a human being is submerged and a feeling of identity with the subject takes its place. This is a common experience I believe and while it is but the beginning of intellectual adventure it appears to be the secret to understanding, particularly when the subjects are organisms. If you bring your mind and senses close enough and long enough to any creature from jellyfish to monkey, sooner or later it begins to explain itself in a manner you can understand but may have trouble in translating into language. In some degree I know this to be true.

If the nature of the mind is best shown by those activities it most enjoys and that bring it greatest satisfaction, we must include with the craving to understand the nature of matter, energy and life as we know them in the present, the urge to comprehend time and history. Left alone we are as much concerned with digging into the past as we are with watching galaxies over the rim of night or peering into a living cell, all of them arduous occupations in their own particular ways although fascinating beyond description. But we reach for time as much as space, and all that it contains—and all for the sake of understanding and self-identification.

We are drawn in spirit toward the past as if by a magnet, concerned with all life since we ourselves are alive, but searching above all for our own image. Yet we feel ourselves always as being in the present, as though time itself were moving and we move with it. And we look into and have hope for the future, as if it were real and only our dim sight were at fault for seeing so little. Yet I think everyone of us realises there is an illusion somewhere—that we are somehow poised on the crest of eternity where time as we are accustomed to speak of it has no meaning.

The illusion is that we live in the present. The truth is that we live and that there is no present. In the second it takes to read this sentence what you felt to be present became the past, and the future became the present and now that has gone too. Yet the sentence existed, though only as a process or activity in your mind. It existed, as you yourself exist, from beginning to end. I cannot tell whether the point I am making is subtle or obvious, but I know of nothing more vital to my own comprehension of what I believe to be reality. When you hum or hear a melody no momentary note has any meaning by itself and only the whole sequential pattern constitutes the tune for, as Whitehead said, the process itself is the actuality.

You realise this in the case of yourself. You are not just what you are at this particular instant, you consist of all that goes on within you, especially within your mind, throughout the day. Your day's activity, mental and physical, is a part of you and by extension you are all that you have ever been— like an unfinished symphony. Each one of us I believe feels this sense of continuity. We may at times forget our childhood and our growing up, but usually not for long and in any case it is all there in what we feel but cannot demonstrate to be a living form. This I think is the reality, and not that yesterday is dead and gone; and I believe that this remains true whether memory is at work or not. From the time of our first conscious awakening the seeds of the mind have been growing, fed by the senses throughout the years of growth; some of the flowers are vivid but most are fertile and can bring forth fruit if properly stimulated. And as any biography will show, the child is in the man and only the whole life makes any kind of sense.

I believe that the human mind instinctively recognises all of this, in spite of fallacies our language interposes, and that during the closing notes of an individual life the question, if any, should be not do I have an immortal soul and what comes next, but how much of a soul have I grown? Whether individual consciousness persists or not—and personally I would only willingly accept it on certain terms—all that lives, all that has lived, retains its value and its meaning. My own language fails me here, for the thought that presses upon me has never been fully spoken although I think it is a common feeling, as if words have ways of their own and refuse to carry certain loads. Yet to put it briefly but imperfectly: I believe the past lives, that the present is eternal, and the future immanent; that we take it as an indivisible whole and that our obsession with the sweep and drama of history, our probing with fossils and other symbols of time, and our efforts to construct theories of evolution of life and matter, are all in keeping with the craving to recreate in the human mind the unity of the universe in all its dimensions. The fact that we are so concerned and make such attempts to do this is much more significant than the results we may obtain. Space and time unite in the mind, in the organism, and in the universe as one all-inclusive whole. You cannot think of thought or of life or of atoms except as patterns of behavior in a four-dimensional universe, for, to use Whitehead's words again, there is no Nature in an instant.

The consequences of this manner of thinking are considerable, for it is a way of looking at things which emphasizes certain concepts and values. It permeates modern physics and it is slowly transforming biological science. An organism, whether animal or plant, is no longer something concrete with a certain structure, color and shape, but is an event or activity of a certain kind which is both continuous and forever changing. The chicken is both the egg and the hen and all that lies between; in fact it is more than this for the identity of the egg is lost in its parent and the hen has a future immanent in its own eggs—and yet it is all one. You can no more take time away from life than you can take away one of the three spatial dimensions.

As individuals we each contain within us the whole of our individual existence. As humanity we not only add up in a queerly collective sense but embrace the past as well. Man is the whole fantastic event which includes not only what we call the present, together with its potentiality, but also all that has gone before that can be recognised as human, which in turn takes roots in a more extensive being. That we are delving for it so is the same urge, I feel sure, as most people get during their middle or later years to recapture the days of their youth. We know instinctively that it is part of us and not merely idle curiosity, for the desire to repossess, both in the individual and in science, is usually passionate. Yet there is no place that I can see where we can draw a line. The individual becomes one with his species, the species with its kind, and so ever-broadening in space and deepening in time all life becomes one. We are but a phase of it, and a recent one. In essence this is simply the theory of evolution, although that is so much more than a theory for it is primarily our acknowledgement of the unity and the continuity of life. And to me at least it means that the living quality of the human creatures who struggled through the ice age is real, although I can barely sense it; that the age of early mammals is still real because it has already happened; and that the earlier events in the history of earthly life, however vague our notions of them may be, still retain their value. We can find analogy in a symphony, although it is much more than an analogy.

A symphony is a single event from beginning to end, an indivisible whole. Its parts may be separately enjoyable and beautiful but are necessarily incomplete when heard in isolation, while the whole has a content and a majesty which is more than the simple addition of the values and properties of the individual parts. All this is fully recognized. Moreover this is true whether we are considering a symphony as it grew within the creative intensity of a Beethoven or as a re-creation in the mind of a conductor or through the ears of the listeners. The opening movement is not dead and gone because you are listening to later phrases, and the closing measures are only the development of what has already happened. It remains a unity in time or it has no meaning at all, and its musical life is in the whole of it—without present, past or future but only eternal beauty. And I believe this is as true of the total pageant of life as it is of this symphonic expression of life. The past is alive in the same sense as the first part of the symphony; we represent a refrain somewhere along the course; and whether our particular refrain evolves into the major movement or gives way to another is of more concern to us than to the whole: in any case we have been heard and consequently remain immortal. This may be the faith of an individual but it also makes sense, particularly to those who study the development of organisms and are forced to think in four dimensions.

It makes sense in more ways than one, for it also gives reason to my being. I am living my life for the sake of living and not for any thought of entering pearly gates. All that I can be I will be, but for the sake of being. I know that work, love, hope, the search for beauty, self discipline, the vigorous use of reason, all are immediately satisfying and require no justification or purpose other than themselves. The quality of life is paramount and we need to hold to our old concepts of greatness and to cultivate our human garden for its finest flowers.

In the end I believe it is reason that reigns supreme. I do not mean that process of logical reasoning which is a tool of conscious thought but that part of you which craves to understand and, having understood, accepts and governs accordingly. Man is a rational being, much more rational than is generally admitted, but he seems somewhat afraid to trust his reason. Psychoanalysts for instance, who generally fail to acknowledge the role of reason, cure by means of explanation wherever they cure at all, for once reason understands, it creates order where there had been confusion. Potentially it is master of the subconscious hungers of the self. A man under hypnotic influence may give away all his possessions or even accuse himself of a crime which results in his execution, but he will not violate what to him is a moral principle—his sense of right is greater than his instinct for self-preservation. And in industry it is well known that a man will work better under bad conditions than under unjust conditions no matter how physically good the last may be. We are rational in a way that is new in this world, and our reason has the power to govern the whole human personality.

We are underestimating both the craving and the capacity of human beings everywhere to understand the meaning of things, the nature of our world and ourselves, and our particular predicament as individuals and societies. Unless warped and deafened and deadened by propaganda the average human individual has resources and capacities that should cause a tyrant shame. If information is true, or as true as can be, understanding begins and the will to act according to the light eventually follows. I doubt if a collective will is ever very potent but the individual will is powerful indeed and it is vital that it comes from minds whose understanding is based on truth. And inasmuch as each individual view of the truth is inevitably a little different from all others, we need to integrate them for greater wisdom. The collective pool of understanding grows from what is poured into it, but the contributions are those of individuals and the will to act must come from them—as the diversified individuals of a group acting together like those of an orchestra, not as members of a herd following the loudest voice.

We need faith, a faith in ourselves as human beings and not as members of this or that race or religion or state or class of society. We need no faith in supernatural forces. We need only to recognise that our knowledge of the universe through our senses and our knowledge of the universe through our own inward nature show that it is orderly, moral and beautiful, that it is akin to intelligence, that love and hope belong in it as fully as light itself, and that the power and will of the human mind is but a symptom of reality; that we, when we are most human, most rational, most aware of love and beauty, reflect and represent the spirit of the universe. That should be enough. But insofar as we recognize this and fail to live accordingly, we know and do evil in some degree, for the deeper the insight the greater the sin.

22

STAR OF DESTINY

I CANNOT, any more than you, see through the storms which loom ahead. As an individual with a one-track mind I can merely show you the distance we have already come and indicate the direction we sail in. We have come so far we cannot falter now and for the long run there are signs that draw us onward. Nor are we entirely without means of navigation.

Our present strength and such glory as we have, come from our transcending those somewhat lesser humans that lived so many years before us. At least ten thousand years ago we reached, as individuals, a physical and mental stature not measurably different from what we have at present, and the episode we have been enjoying since the neolithic world began is essentially an exploitation of our particular stage of individual evolution. We are exploring and exploiting the qualities and capacities of our existing state—seeing oneself in the eyes of others, doing all that we can with what we have and are, and building social structures with the present human bricks. It is fun of a kind though it is getting pretty rough. But whether we can understand much more than we do of the nature of things and what it is all about, without improving our individual quality, I am not at all sure.

Since reason governs so well when it understands the circumstances and has such a yearning to comprehend, our lack of understanding and our troubles must come largely from the limitations arising from immaturity. We are confused about almost everything, but our confusion is essentially human and is hardly the kind we share with the rest of the animal kingdom; it marks us off, so that there is much truth in the statement that man's toughest problem is himself. The real trouble however is not that we are human but that we are not human enough, and the problem now is to define the essence of that humanity, to see what it means to be more human, and how we may possibly arrive at such a state. It is just as much a scientific problem as was that of releasing atomic energy or the unsolved problem of discovering the nature and cure of cancer. The fact that human destiny is bound up with success or failure in this instance is beside the point. Nor does the inclusion of values make much difference. The idea common in scientific and other intellectual circles that science has nothing to do with values has been unfortunate and damaging, for it has tended to exclude the possibility of any scientific understanding of human experience itself. Science, apart from its practical exploitation, is no more materialistic than the humanities or religion and is just as much concerned with the ultimate meaning of things whether of matter or mind. The scientific technique of putting questions in certain ways and expecting answers in certain terms is merely one of methodical expediency. There is no barrier beyond which inquiry cannot be pushed, simply because prior claims have been made, and if science enters the field of the spirit, so much the better for the scientists, especially those who like to be thought tough-minded. The truth in any case cannot suffer.

Being human concerns both body and soul. To be more human equally concerns them both. It is even hard to consider one without the other. The amount of time we have as individuals, the kind of time we have, all the faculties of the mind, and all that comprises the personality are bound up together. This is the way it has been and such is the way I believe it will continue.

To become more human may or may not mean living for a longer period of calendar time. It certainly would mean an increase in the amount of biological time. And by extrapolation from the past million years it would also mean a larger brain. These two changes would be mandatory, first concerning life and the other mind, for these are the only two biological distinctions that separate us from other mammals, at least so far as I can see.

Bernard Shaw came to the conclusion that the trouble with human beings is that they never grow up. They mature so slowly that they are still irresponsible adolescents at the time of their death—and who will gainsay him? The solution he proposed in 'Back to Methuselah' was that we should somehow extend the span of life to three hundred years, which should allow us to attain emotional and intellectual maturity and give us so much time to endure upon the earth that we would take more care of things and act less like transients in a rooming house. In any case, for whatever reason, the desire to extend our lives seems to be strangely and strongly ingrained, either as thoughts of personal immortality or expressed in actual attempts to prolong existence by means of tissue extracts. Forecasts are frequently made that the postponement of individual death by another fifty years is one of those scientific marvels that wait around the corner, like landing on the moon or coaxing the earth to support ten billion human beings. For we like to dream.

Yet some dreams mean more than others, though no one has so far put Humpty-Dumpty together again or ever will. If we take care of a machine and drive carefully we may keep it going beyond the usual run, but not for very long and not for any very useful purpose. Living beyond our time will always be tiresome and I think we waste our effort in looking for ways to keep old worn-out bodies and minds together. The fountain of youth flows from the beginning of life, not from its end.

To be human means to be youthful and joyful in spirit, which makes some people less human than others. And we are youthful for a longer time than any other creature, far longer even than those who live to a comparable age. Much of the quality of life which we cherish most comes from this, the freshness and eagerness of mind that stays with the lucky ones most of their lives. To be more human demands a longer and more thorough going youthfulness which I believe can come only in the way it came before. We need to be stretched even further between conception and death. If instead of trying to add unwanted years to the aged person we manage to slow the rate of growth and postpone puberty from fifteen years to the age of twenty or even thirty, what would it mean to the length and quality of life? It would be no greater a physiological step than the one we have already taken from the ape and is no more fantastic a thought than what has so far happened. If the life span should be uniformly affected, puberty at twenty would mean, for the female, menopause at sixty and death at the century mark instead of seventy-five. Puberty at thirty would mean menopause at ninety and death from old age at one hundred and fifty—Methuselahs indeed. Yet I suspect and hope it would work out a little differently, for it is possible that doubling the age at which puberty is reached would not necessarily double the life span as a whole, that it might happen that the living elastic would stretch more at the younger end than at the old and we could retain our youth for a longer time than we would have to pay for in aged years.

I have chosen these figures for their simple arithmetic, not for any other reason. I may be overestimating or underestimating what is possible, for there is no way to tell. But I am certain of this: that a mechanism exists whereby life can be extended in the sense I have indicated, or else we would not be what we already are. And if it has worked so far, it conceivably can be made to go on working if it is not doing so even now—the wheel turns so slowly that in any case we cannot sense its motion. Yet feasibility is something distinct from desirability and it is the last that concerns me at the moment. What the overall effects of such a change would be are difficult to estimate. They would be vast, to say the least, but they cannot be discussed as though no other changes had taken place, no matter how enticing the vistas may appear to be for mental exercising or even dreams. Clearly the whole of life would be altered in a deeply intensifying manner.

Our brains have grown as much as have the youthful quality and time of our individual lives, and they have grown to a larger extent than is shown by the dimensions of a head. Brains have expanded greatly in area but have puckered and folded to keep within bounds, and the cortex may now be twice as large as it was in mid-Ice-age men, and larger than it was in a Neanderthal. We cannot tell what change, if any, there has been since the ice melted away ten thousand years ago. Yet whether we have lost motion or not, the possibility remains that in the course of evolutionary time an expanding brain can still go on expanding. It is possible that our brains can continue to improve without further expansion, by a process of refinement of the already exquisite architectural detail they now possess, or we may have reached the limit in this respect and the next step, if there is to be one, is necessarily to expand once more.

Supposing it does, what then? It depends on how much and in what way. You can see the range already in the present scale, for we have musicians' brains, painters' brains, mathe-

maticians' and philosophers' brains, not to mention all those
who serve but stand and wait. Each small variation seems to
carry insight and a sort of genius of its own, all of which we
recognise. We are aware of the insights, aware of beauty when
we take time to look at it; we are consciously aware of love,
hope, compassion and ethics, and we are vaguely aware of much
more that we cannot possibly put into words. We are aware
of a lot and we are aware of our limits, and this is the point.
Somewhere in the course of our glacial ascent these qualities
and powers of the mind and spirit emerged into conscious
presence, though just when we will never know since there
are also limits to what a fossil skull can say about a mind it
once enclosed. But not too long ago in terms of our true history
all these most human properties were in a state of emergence
which we would hardly recognize, although the roots went
deep. As our brains have grown so has the power of reason and
with it all have come these strange new lights we call the spirit.
And by this token if our brains continue to evolve in the same
general manner as they have in the past, the new capacity for
understanding and new illuminations may flood in far beyond
anything we can at present conceive. The essential human qualities of the mind are already new in kind. Those that would
appear might be just as strange and far more wonderful, while
those which are here or immanent may blossom beyond recognition. This may be faith but it is based on reason.

Extension of life and enlargement of brain I believe go hand
in hand, though not because of any close relationship but as
the result of a peculiar set of biological circumstances. Think
back for a minute over the interminable generations during
which intelligence has been at a premium, during which there
has been a steady selection in favor of the more intelligent population groups. The outcome through the course of time has
been a steady trend toward larger and larger brains with their
enhanced intelligence. This is no more than the usual way

natural pressures work upon living populations, given time enough to produce results. The peculiar circumstances are of another sort.

The great test of intelligence as a factor of survival value throughout all the rigors of our dawning humanity has been at or after the age of puberty when children assumed the dangers and responsibilities of the work of men and women. Until that age they have always been more or less well protected and sustained and the dull of wit might survive as well as any other. After puberty the tests begin in earnest. This age, which represents the full attainment of brain or head size, and its associated intelligence, is important, for it is at this stage of individual growth that the selective forces in human evolution have been operating most forcibly. This is where the human egg attains its full development.

The other circumstance concerns birth. The maximum size of the head of a baby at birth is determined by the width of the mother's pelvis, and the female human skeleton seems to have made all the adjustment possible to facilitate matters, adjustments that were made long ago. Small-headed babies might be born more easily but they more than likely would grow into ineffective adults. Babies with heads too large at the time of birth would never get born at all, nor under any but recent times would the mother have survived the attempt. Accordingly. once the obstetrical limit had been reached, the problem was how to produce individuals with brains relatively much larger than those produced at birth.

We ourselves are evidence that a solution was found. It was essentially a simple one, although you need to visualise the process of growth to see it. We are concerned in fact with what is virtually a case of ballistics: the missile, the human egg; the objective, an individual with a head and brain of a certain size; the problem, to reach the objective in spite of restriction at a certain time and place, namely birth. Now while the size of the human egg is minute and is fixed within very narrow limits, its potentials vary in almost every conceivable way and the potentials for growth of the body as a whole and the brain in particular are among them. But there are two methods by which an egg or embryo can grow to a larger than average size: it can grow faster or it can grow for a longer time. In fact it can even grow more slowly and still end up larger if only it keeps on growing.

Here is the story as I think it has happened. It may be a little repetitious but the superstructure needs a good foundation. To begin with there were mammals who produced young as litters, and the slowest to develop and last to get out were the losers. Then came our arboreal phase where only one young at a time was produced for the sake of subsequent safety—and with no more competition there was no longer any hurry, for the last was first and the first was last. It was not only safer within the womb but the longer birth could be delayed the more advanced would the offspring be. Yet nine months seems to be the limit, both for apes and man, and after that the union tissues simply fail to hold and, ready or not, birth must occur. As the demands of nature for bigger brains grew greater, as she favored the more intelligent as the fathers and mothers of the race, the embryos tending to develop the largest heads within the nine month period became the most successful adults—but only up to a certain point! Once head-size at birth reached the limit of size permitted by the pelvic opening, no further increase at the time of birth was possible. Building bigger brains by starting to build them sooner or by building on a larger embryonic scale to begin with or by forcing the pace of growth all resulted in a lethal jam and another way had to be discovered.

The only remaining answer to nature's pressure for adults with ever larger brains was to prolong growth farther beyond the time of birth, and the longer the period could be extended the larger the head and the brain would be. And individuals thus produced, slowly and carefully during a long period of time, were most likely superior in other ways, simply as organisms. With each small increase in adult brain size the time between birth and puberty also lengthened. It had to, just to make the larger brain. And step by step, each one infinitisimal as each generation succeeded the last, we took our distinctively human path. Our long infancy, drawn-out childhood, prolonged youth and delayed puberty are simply the means by which our big skulls and voluminous brains could be attained, and the prolongation of life as a whole is its consequence. The human mind is born of human infancy and it is no wonder that sometimes it seems to trail its cloud of glory.

This is not just an account of the past and an explanation of the present, it is also our hope for the future. As long as there is a continuing need for our brains to improve and accordingly become larger, and as long as we do not too disastrously interfere with the process of selection, we will continue to acquire larger brains by the only way we have been able to gain them in the past. We will get larger brains, more intelligence, greater insights, and more extended childhood, longer youth and lengthened lives in a single stream, though the stream move but slowly. There is much to look forward to, if only we can look far enough. For unless we can discern a short cut we may be looking forward as far as we have been looking backward, to a time not less than several hundred thousand years away. We are inclined to say that this is too far ahead to worry about, but the inclination itself is merely an expression of our present limitations. We are struggling to embrace time in both directions but our reach is short. It would be most human to extend it, for such is the quality of our mind that it wants eternity.

I cannot foresee in any specific way what life might be if human beings were not too many but were individually longer and more youthful living and endowed with minds with powers of understanding beyond our conception, except that all that is now immanent within us would be wonderfully expressed— that what we see in the mirror darkly we would then see face to face. If such is our destiny, even as a remote possibility, we should never lose sight of it, for as a star to steer by it beckons brightly.

Meanwhile we are here, looking over our shoulder and hoping for a future, for mankind at least, if not for much else. I think we see something of the way we have come and however dimly, the way it takes us. Having come so far already, we owe loyalty to the past that has brought us here, and that loyalty is inclusive. If we continue to squander all the riches of the earth within a few human generations, as I fear we will, we should at least do it knowingly as the spendthrifts we are, knowing that we cheat our descendants of a heritage that should have been theirs as much as ours. At the best I suppose we are removing certain temptations to easy living that we ourselves would have been better without. I am more disturbed however at the voracity of our exploitation than the fact of utilisation of accumulated reserves, for it suggests too strongly the more unpleasant qualities of spoiled children of any age who expect everything, expect it to last forever, and give nothing. The earth is not ours. We belong to the earth and we must come down to earth to find our place. It will not be easy.

We are far more in jeopardy from our success than from any possibility of failure, if success means continually increasing the size of the human population, utilizing natural resources, manufacturing things nature never dreamed of, and pushing all life that is not useful off the face of the earth. We have the power perhaps to do all of these things, but where is the wisdom? We may become more intelligent in the way we do them. Instead of lumbering by cut and burn methods, for instance, forests are getting to be regarded more as standing crops with an annual yield. It is a larger and more sensible view which is far more profitable if anything but immediate returns is contemplated. But the basic attitude remains unchanged.

When men were all hunters or food gatherers and human communities were small, human beings lived as a part of nature. They knew and felt it intuitively for nature engulfed them. In primitive societies even now this understanding prevails. Yet the more our cities grow, the more we manufacture within walls of our own construction, the more we dig into the ground or plant food crops for purely human sustenance, the more everything that is wild seems to fade from sight. We look at a wood and think what could we do with it. If a wild animal is seen by a man with a gun it gets shot. Usually when anyone is shown some strange small creature or even some that are not so strange the response is what good is it? The sense of community has been lost, and until we regain it I think we are lost too, for in this attitude we are attacking our own roots. But so long as we attempt to insert more and more people into the earth's frame everything else goes by the board, to survive as best it can as flotsam in the remote shallows of existence. We cheat ourselves as well as our successors.

Man is a wild animal and the earth is wild. We obscure the facts by putting buildings, roads and fences between us and the rest of creation, but the wildness remains even in the heart of a city when no other sign of the natural world can be seen. Cities may have civilized mankind several thousand years ago but now that they have become worlds in themselves, either alone or by extension, from which there is no real escape, the inherent wildness of young humanity becomes more and more evident. We have domesticated certain animals by tipping the balance from brain to brawn, so that we have too little need to consider the feelings of a cow or a sheep—the dog is a companion, which is different. But man himself is not tamed, not as a whole although to the extent that he may become so at times he loses his essential spirit. Few men are as savage as city-bred tyrants can be, which is a problem we have to cope with, but the basic wildness that lies somewhere in the heart of each of us is the greatest guarantee that we will one day work through our artificial world to one in keeping with the living whole.

It is a hard way of progress, but when conditions become intolerable, whether from too much of anything from regimentation to television or too little sustenance of either bodily or spiritual kind, a rebellion of some sort eventually breaks out. In the end excesses will be self-defeating. In view of this do we have to wait till defeat is imposed upon us? It would be wiser to come to terms while we still have some choice.

We do have the choice, at least to some extent. We can set limits, if we can control ourselves, to the quantity of humanity so that a margin is left on the earth for something besides bread and human beings. We can decide whether the margin for life and beauty other than our own shall be large or small. And we can encourage the growth of this kind of person rather than that, and of these plants and creatures rather than those. We can choose between quality and quantity in all things. The choice is ours and so in the course of time, if we look beyond our own individual life time, will be the consequences.

Yet the choice will never be easy. If we decide eventually in favor of quality, then we assume the power and the burden of judgment, for when total life is limited a favor to one is restriction to others. The circumstances are not unlike a garden of which part is for the kitchen and part for wonder, although this suggests at least as much control over the nature of things as a good gardener possesses. This we do not have, in spite of appearances to the contrary, and in any case this point of view is only one step better than of man as a manager or miner. The earth may be a garden, though no longer an Eden, but we are not the gardener. We are its growth, from which at present it is suffering. We are a selfconscious growth it is true and we seem to want to cut ourself free, but so far as we succeed I think we lose our soul.

I have said that man is wild and will always in the end rebel at what he cannot stand, which is insurance against any deadening crystallization of human society. But nature also is wild and is nonetheless wild for being trampled underfoot. Nothing is so wild as a virus, a weed or an insect and at times I feel that even the rocks themselves are wild. And if both man and nature are wild and if man continues to oppose himself to nature as he now is doing, then we are in for a kind of unpredictable game for as long as we can last. In the end we would lose and nature would take over without us.

What is it that we recognise in wildness? I think that more than an unquenchable drive it is essentially this quality of unpredictability which defies control. It goes to the heart of the man-nature relationship and is as much a fact of life to be accepted as is birth and death. It means that the whole is always greater than the part and that man as a part of nature can never fully comprehend the whole. This I think is fortunate, for it ensures an unending quest and is proof that it is the journey that matters and not the goal. It means that any situation involving both man and nature will always contain elements unforeseen by human understanding, that whenever we act to change a situation or set of circumstances in a certain way, we succeed in making a change but not the one we planned on. We employ antibiotics to kill off disease-causing viruses or disease-bearing insects and for awhile feel that we have everything under control; then new and tougher strains of viruses appear in place of those we pushed aside, while starvation sweeps the birds and fish that fed upon the insects and crops fail from lack of pollination. We can always be wise in hindsight but I am convinced we will never foresee the full consequences of any action we may be inclined to take. Therefore we have to retain intelligence and adaptability and play along always with a minimum of interference with the scheme of things. As an incorporated part of nature we can live wonderfully within her, but as a self-ejected outcast turning to fence with the living earth, we are outmatched from the start. I am speaking neither in parables nor similes. This earth is a living planet, although it is alive in ways that we do not fully comprehend, and unless we conform to the rules of life we are in danger both from within and without. When efficiency is less a fetish, when to be alive signifies more than getting from here to there, when idleness is no longer boredom but opportunity, when there is time for listening, when cornflowers and poppies belong in the wheat, only then will we know that we are re-entering our heritage.

Finally, as in the beginning and always, the individual stands stark and real within the tortured movements of the crowd. Each has joy and sorrow, triumphs and misery, each begins and comes to an end. Every individual now alive or who has ever lived has meaning. I know that insofar as I am a whole man I am all of me from the beginning until now. I also know, also intuitively rather than by reason, that lives that have gone have some eternal quality independent of whether I or anyone else now realise they had ever been. I know that what I did and felt yesterday, which was so intense and vital yesterday, is not less significant because today is another day. I come again and again to realise that the process itself is the reality, that creation is creating, whether it be writing a letter, caring for a child, or any other piece of living. And if such living can only exist in time, it can never be lost in time. I cannot prove this but perhaps it will ring a bell.

By all that I can sense, think or feel, I know that what is

embraced between birth and death can have all the meaning in the world, though how much depends not on being born but on the nature of the life which follows. That it is less important to attain a better world than it is to strive for it, that it is better to create than to have, that short periods of intensive awareness mean more than any amount of dullness, that the quality of transcending growth and newness is the quality of life—these are the notes of the symphony, which are never lost because they have happened. And if this fumbling for expression is anywhere near the mark, the fumbling itself becomes merely evidence of the fragmentary nature of the small part which tries to comprehend the whole.

Each individual life is its own creation, its own cycle of renewal which from the nature of things must have a temporal end. Each of us has the chance to make a lot or a little out of our own potentiality and the time we have to grow in, but sooner or later the growth must become self-directing. When the striving ceases, growth is over and the human essence which is the spirit of youth disappears or dies, leaving old disillusion in its place. We can, as individuals, increase the content of humanity here and now, and without increasing the quantity of human beings. The need gets greater all the time.

As the average age of the human population rises and as the chances improve that every individual born will live out his or her life to its natural end, both the need and the difficulty of retaining the zest for life increases. A dreary dullness is a more deadly threat in the end than even atomic war, and it can be brought on by gaining more years than the spirit can carry, just as readily as by oppressive regimentation, smothering indoctrination, chasing pleasure, or too hard a struggle for bare existence. At the same time we cannot wait upon any such actual prolongation of youth into age as may be our eventual destiny, for this change is already with us. This is no challenge for posterity, it is here facing us and we and our children have to realise that seventy or eighty years of living can hold a lot of life, and that empty shells are not worth keeping.

Age in all its aspects is the cessation of growth. Youth is retained by everything that grows. These are biological statements which apply to all organisms. They apply to the mind and spirit as well as to the body. And every child starts with the capacity if not the opportunity to unfold and to turn every experience of living into new growth, perhaps with joy, perhaps with pain, but nevertheless into growth. The senses of childhood are open to beauty and wonder, the heart to hope, the mind to question. The instinct is toward love and laughter, compassion and kindness, to live in the light and by the light. Who quenches it? I suppose chiefly those who have already lost it all. But the growing spirit or personality can keep on growing throughout its days until at last the body is held together by nothing else. It is possible to live serenely in the midst of turmoil, to keep your true face open to all men; it is possible to fight for the life of your mind as much as your body, to know that ideals are but glimpses of truth, that truth is beauty and love is harmony and that evil comes from losing them. All this has been said before, and some have died for saying it. It is high time now that we listen.

The rules are simple but hard to follow: to determine what your values are and to live by them—when a man has that much wisdom and courage his stature is usually such that we all acknowledge it, knowing that there for the grace of man we should go too; to have faith in the power of those ideas which represent the truth and to be patient; to keep open the windows to beauty, which will always pass our understanding; and to love all life and the earth itself in humility, respect and wonder. There is richness here if only we will give ourselves to being alive and cease struggling to disown our nature. The meaning of meekness is generally misinterpreted, for the meek who will one day inherit the earth will be only outwardly quiet, having learned the foolishness of wasteful strife with either men or facts. Within they will enjoy a serene intensity of awareness and creative thought that even now comes through to some of us once in a while. When it does we call them master.

FOR FURTHER READING

AGNES ARBOR. *The Mind and the Eye.* Cambridge.

ANTHONY BARNETT. *The Human Species.* W. W. Norton.

BRUCE BLIVEN. *Preview of Tomorrow.* A. A. Knopf.

HARRISON BROWN. *The Challenge of Man's Future.* Viking.

C. E. P. BROOKS. *Climate Through the Ages.* Benn.

ERNST CASSIRER. *An Essay on Man.* Doubleday, Anchor.

V. GORDON CHILDE. *Man Makes Himself.* Mentor.

SONIA COLE. *The Prehistory of East Africa.* Pelican.

ROBERT C. COOK. *Human Fertility.* Sloane.

CARLETON S. COON. *The Story of Man.* A. A. Knopf.

NORMAN COUSINS. *Who Speaks for Man?* Macmillan.

C. G. DARWIN. *The Next Million Years.* Hart, Davies.

H. J. FLEURE. *A Natural History of Man in Britain.* Collins.

JACQUETTA HAWKES. *A Land.* Cresset.

JULIAN HUXLEY. *Man in the Modern World.* Mentor.

F. G. JUENGER. *The Failure of Technology.* Henry Regnery (Humanist).

CLYDE KLUCKHOLN. *Mirror for Man.* Whittlesey, McGraw-Hill.

JOSEPH WOOD KRUTCH. *Measure for Man.* Bobbs, Merrill.

CLARENCE MUMFORD. *The Conduct of Life.* Harcourt-Brace.

J. ROBERT OPPENHEIMER. *Science and the Common Understanding.* Simon & Schuster.

FAIRFIELD OSBORN. *This Plundered Planet*. Little, Brown.

FAIRFIELD OSBORN. *The Limits of the Earth*. Little, Brown.

RODERICK SEIDENBERG. *Post-historic Man*. Univ. North Carolina.

HARLOW SHAPLEY. *Climatic Change*. Harvard.

CHARLES SHERRINGTON. *Man on his Nature*. Doubleday, Anchor.

G. G. SIMPSON. *The Meaning of Evolution*. Mentor.

HOMER SMITH. *Man and his Gods*. Little, Brown.

HOMER SMITH. *From Fish to Philosopher*. Little, Brown.

H. SPENCER-JONES. *Life on Other Worlds*. Mentor.

L. DUDLEY STAMP. *Land for Tomorrow*. Indiana U.P.

LAURA THOMPSON. *Culture in Crisis*, (Hopi). Harper.

WILLIAM VOGT. *The Road to Survival*. Sloane.

A. N. WHITEHEAD. *Adventures in Ideas*. Pelican.

R. J. WILLIAMS. *Free and Unequal*. Univ. Texas.

LEONARD WOOLLEY. *Ur of the Chaldees*. Pelican.

FREDERICK ZEUNER. *Dating the Past*. Methuen.

INDEX